THE LONDON DIPLOMATIC

January 2020

CONTENTS

The data displayed in this document was correct at the time of printing 10/02/2020

(Revised 03/02/2020)

THE LONDON DIPLOMATIC LIST

Alphabetical list of the representatives of Foreign States & Commonwealth Countries in London with the names & designations of the persons returned as composing their Diplomatic Staff. Representatives of Foreign States & Commonwealth Countries & their Diplomatic Staff enjoy privileges & immunities under the Diplomatic Privileges Act, 1964. Except where shown, private addresses are not available.

m   Married
*   Married but not accompanied by wife or husband

AFGHANISTAN

Embassy of the Islamic Republic of Afghanistan

31 Princes Gate SW7 1QQ
0207 225 4743
Email:ea@afghanistanembassy.org.uk
www.afghanistanembassy.org.uk
Monday-Friday 09:00 -17:00

Consular Department
0207 225 4748
consulate@afghanistanembassy.org.uk
Monday-Friday 09:00-17:00

HIS EXCELLENCY MR SAID TAYEB JAWAD **m** *Ambassador Extraordinary & Plenipotentiary (since 24 April 2017)*
    Mrs Shamim Jawad
Mr Abdul Khaliq Samandary **m** *Counsellor*
Mr M Hanif Ahmadzai **m** *Counsellor*
Mr Haroon Naderi **m** *Military Attaché*
Mr Naveed Noormal **m** *1st Secretary*
Mr Sayed Mansoor Sayed **m** *1st Secretary*
Mrs Aqila Rahmani *2nd Secretary*
Mrs Homaira Sadat Dashti **m** *2nd Secretary*
Mr Faramaz Hussiny *3rd Secretary*
Mr Zikrullah Mahmoodi **m** *Deputy Military Attache*

ALBANIA

Embassy of the Republic of Albania
33 St George's Drive SW1V 4DG
020 7828 8897
Fax 020 7828 8869
embassy.london@mfa.gov.al
http://www.ambasadat.gov.al/united-kingdom/

Consular Section
020 7828 8897
Fax 020 7828 8869
consular.london@mfa.gov.al

Defence Attaché's Office
020 7828 8897
Fax 020 7828 8869
aulonder@mod.gov.al

Police Liaison Officer's Office
020 7828 8897
Fax 020 7828 8869
andrin.cenaj@asp.gov.al

HIS EXELLENCY MR QIRJAKO QIRKO * *Ambassador Extraordinary & Plenipotentiary* (since 26 *August 2016*)
    Mrs Anxhela Qirko
Mrs Alketa Lama * *Counsellor (Political Affairs)*
Mr Refik Golli *2nd Secretary Consul (Consular Services)*
Colonel Edmond Sardi m *Defence Attaché*
Andrin Cenaj m *Liaison Officer (Police Liaison)*

ALGERIA

People's Democratic Republic of Algeria
1-3 Riding House Street W1W 7DR
Tel 00 44 20 7299 7077
Fax 00 44 20 7299 7076
info@algerianembassy.org.uk

Consular Section
The Portal, 5 Portal Way, London W3 6RS
Tel00 44 20 8752 1177
Fax 00 44 20 8752 8061
info@algerian-consulate.org.uk

HIS EXCELLENCY MR ABDERRAHMANE BENGUERRAH m *Ambassador Extraordinary & Plenipotentiary (since 8 November 2019)*
    Mrs Fatiha BENGUERRAH
Mr Mourad Louhaidia m *Minister-Counsellor & Deputy Head of Mission*
Mr Abdelkrim Beha m *Consul General*
Colonel Malik Mustapha Lebboukh m *Defence Attaché*
Mr Mostefa Boudib m *Minister Plenipotentiary*
Mr Ammar Karabadja m *Counsellor*
Lt Colonel Khaled Reghioua m *Maritime Attaché*
Mr Mohamed Khelifi m *Counsellor*
Mr Mohamed Seghir Benghanem m *Counsellor*
Mr Abdenour Gasmi m *Counsellor (Chancery Attaché)*
Mr Djamel Alaouchiche m *1st Secretary*
Mr Belaid Raked m *1st Secretary*
Mr Mokhtar Latrache m *1st Secretary (Chancery Attaché)*
Mr Hamed Oussama Salhi *1st Secretary*
Mr Ishak Dehibi m *1st Secretary*
Mrs Imen Dehibi m *1st Secretary*
Mrs Nassima Morsli m *1st Secretary*
Mrs Samia Laadjal Adjal m *Attaché*
Mrs Sihem Zibra m *Attaché*
Mr Youcef Bezzala m *Attaché*
Mr Mabrouk Feddaoui m *Attaché*
Mr Abdenour Seddi m *Attaché*

ANDORRA

The Principality of Andorra
Ministry of Foreign Affairs & Institutional Relations, C/ Prat de la Creu 62-64, AD500 Andorra la Vella
Tel: +376 875 704
Fax: +376 869 559
Cristina_Mota@govern.ad

Ms Cristina Mota Gouveia *Minister-Counsellor*

ANGOLA

Embassy of the Republic of Angola
22 Dorset Street W1U 6QY

020 7299 9850
Fax 020 7486 9397
embassy@angola.org.uk
Monday-Friday 09.00-12.00 & 13.30-16.00
Visa Section Monday-Friday 09.30-13.00

Consulate General
46 Bedford Square WC1B 3DP
Tel 020 7291 8700
Monday-Friday 09.00-12.00 & 13.00-16.00
Visa Section – 21 Bedford Square Avenue, London WC1B 3AS
Monday-Friday 09.00-17.00

HIS EXCELLENCY MR GERALDO NUNDA **m** *Ambassador Extraordinary & Plenipotentiary (since 15 January 2020)*
Mr. Diogo José Paulo Cristiano **m** *Minister-Counsellor & Chargé d'Affaires a.i.*

Mrs. Vanda Maria Breganha de Lemos Paula Gomes **m** *Minister-Counsellor*

Mr. Bernardino Adão João Pacheco **m** *Counsellor*

Colonel Rui Nelson Gonçalves **m** Defence Attaché

Capitão António Pascoal Chibia **m** Assistant Defence Attaché

Ms. Rosa Benigno F. Sobrinho * Deputy Angolan Representative

Mr. André Manuel Cândido * Vice Consul

Mr. Sebastião dos Santos Kiala **s** Vice Consul & Consul a.i.

Ms. Elianne Tessa G. S. de Carvalho **s** Consular Officer

ANTIGUA AND BARBUDA

High Commission for Antigua and Barbuda
2nd Floor 45 Crawford Place W1H 4LP
020 7258 0070
Fax 020 7258 7486
highcommission@antigua-barbuda.com
www.antigua-barbuda.com

HER EXCELLENCY MS KAREN-MAE HILL *High Commissioner (since* 10 January 2016)
Miss Ideka Arienne Dowe *Economic & Trade Attaché*
Mr Antonio Olsen Joseph *Political, Diaspora & Consular Affairs Attaché*

ARGENTINA

Embassy of the Argentine Republic
65 Brook Street W1K 4AH
020 7318 1300
Fax 020 7318 1301
www.argentine-embassy-uk.org
info@argentine-embassy-uk.org
trade@argentine-embassy-uk.org
culture@argentine-embassy-uk.org
politica@argentine-embassy-uk.org
pressoffice@argentine-embassy-uk.org
protocol@argentine-embassy-uk.org

Consulate General
27 Three Kings Yard W1K 4DF
020 7318 1340

Fax 020 7318 1349
www.clond.mrecic.gov.ar
clond@mrecic.gov.ar

Defence Attaché's Office (Military, Naval & Air Attachés)
134-136 Buckingham Palace Road Second Floor SW1W 9TR
020 7730 4356
Fax 020 77824 8703
defence@argentine-embassy-uk.org

Representation to IMO
27 Three Kings Yard W1K 4DF
020 7318 1340
Fax 020 7318 1349
imo@argentine-embassy-uk.org
raomi@mrecic.gov.ar

HIS EXCELLENCY MR CARLOS SERSALE DI CERISANO m *Ambassador Extraordinary & Plenipotentiary* (since 11 March 2016)
        Mrs Linette de Jager
Mr Holger Martinsen m *Consul General*
Ms Valeria Maria Gonzalez Posse *Minister & Deputy Head of Mission*
Group Captain Marcelo Jose Monetto m *(Defence Attaché)*
Mrs Estela Fernanda Millicay Resquin m *Minister (Political & International Law)*
Mr Nicolás Rebok *Minister (Economic & Trade)*
Mr Gonzalo Ortiz de Zarate m *Minister & Deputy Consul General*
Mrs Mariana Plaza m *Minister (Political)*
Mr Pedro López Godoy m *1st Secretary (Political)*
Mrs Maria de la Paz Garcia Calvo m *1st Secretary (Science and Technology)*
Mr Ricardo Alejandro Morelli Rubio m *2nd Secretary (Legal)*
Mr Facundo Santiago m *2nd Secretary (Cultural)*
Mr Martin Miguel Alemandi 3rd *Secretary*
Mr Adrián Vernis m *Attaché*
Captain Pablo Bonuccelli m *Technical Adviser of Permanent Representation to IMO*
Captain Carlos Esteban Salaburu m *Technical Adviser of Permanent Representation to IMO*
Warren Officer II Luis Daniel Barrionuevo m *(Assistant Defence Attaché)*

ARMENIA

Embassy of the Republic of Armenia
25A Cheniston Gardens W8 6TG
020 7938 5435
Fax 020 7938 2595
armembassyuk@mfa.am
armconsularuk@mfa.am
www.uk.mfa.am

Vacant *Ambassador Extraordinary & Plenipotentiary*

Mr Gagik Kirakosyan m *Charge D'Affaires*
Mr Hrachya Stepanyan m *Counsellor*
Mr Aram Araratyan m *Third Secretary (Political and Economic Affairs)*

AUSTRALIA

HIS EXCELLENCY THE HONOURABLE MR GEORGE BRANDIS QC *High Commissioner (since 3 May 2018)*
Mr Matthew Anderson m *Deputy High Commissioner*
Mr Sridhar Ayyalaraju m *Minister-Counsellor (Management)*
Mr Michael McEvoy *Minister-Counsellor*
Commodore Guy Holthouse m *Head Australian Defence Staff*

4

Commander Jennifer Hurst *Minister-Counsellor (Police Liaison)*
Mr Adam Meyer **m** *Minister-Counsellor (Home Affairs)*
Ms Emily Martin **m** *Minister-Counsellor (Economic)*
Dr Christopher Norwood **m** *Minister-Counsellor (Defence Science&Technology)*
Mr Simon Smalley **m** *Minister-Counsellor (Agriculture)*
Ms Mary Mackay-Martin **m** *Minister-Counsellor (Liaison)*
Ms Jennifer Mackinlay **m** *Minister-Counsellor (Commercial)*
Mr Kyle Naish **m** *Counsellor*
Ms Clara Yoo **m** *Counsellor*
Mr Ian Duckworth **m** *Counsellor*
Ms Christine Shannon **m** *Counsellor*
Mr Daniel Holliday **m** *Counsellor*
Captain Shane Craig **m** *Naval Adviser*
Colonel Suzanne Graham **m** *Army Adviser*
Group Captain David Titheridge **m** *Air Force Adviser*
Mr Thomas Nicholls **m** *Counsellor*
Mr Robert Rushby * *Counsellor (Australian Border Force)*
Ms Naomi Clarke *Counsellor (Defence)*
Mr Michael Evans **m** *Counsellor (Liaison)*
Ms Jane Wood **m** *Counsellor (Defence Materiel)*
Mr Russel Smith **m** *Counsellor (Police Liaison)*
Mr John Napier **m** *Counsellor (Immigration & Border Protection)*
Ms Annalisse Sly *Counsellor (Transport)*
Mr James Went **m** *1st Secretary*
Ms Katie Whitting *1st Secretary*
Ms Claire Went **m** *1st Secretary & Consul*
Mr Ryan Billings **m** *1st Secretary*
Ms Desmene Fielding **m** *1st Secretary*
Mr Gregory MacFarlane **m** *1st Secretary*
Mr Julian De Domenico **m** *1st Secretary*
Mr Stephen Dietz *1st Secretary*
Mr Andrew Yong **m** *1st Secretary*
Mr Michael Abbot **m** *1st Secretary & Consul*
Lt Colonel Lachlan Sinclair **m** *Assistant Army Adviser*
Lt Colonel Anthony Evans **m** *Assistant Defence Adviser*
Wing Commander Leigh Dunnett **m** *Assistant Air Force Adviser*
Commander Neil Cheverton **m** *Assistant Navy Adviser*
Mr Ashley Wygoda **m** *1st Secretary (Police Liaison)*
Mr Scott Mellis **m** *1st Secretary (Police Liaison)*
Ms Angela Brooker **m** *1st Secretary (Immigration)*
Ms Skye Keatinge **m** *1st Secretary (Liaison)*
Mr Darryl Parrish **m** *1st Secretary (Police Liaison)*
Mr Stephen Cook *1st Secretary (Police Liaison)*
Ms Katrina Abood *1st Secretary (Immigration)*
Mr Steven Daher **m** *1st Secretary (Police Liaison)*
Ms Karen Parkes *1st Secretary (Financial Intelligence)*
Ms Kristie-Lee Cressy **m** *1st Secretary (Police Liaison)*
Ms Katrina Pullen *1st Secretary (Home Affairs)*
Ms Suzanne Appeldorff **m** *2nd Secretary*
Ms Bethany Ubulom **m** *2nd Secretary*
Mr Hamish Fejo **m** *2nd Secretary*
Ms Nell Bunce *2nd Secretary (Liaison)*
Ms Janette Niemann *Executive Assistant (Consular)*

AUSTRIA

Embassy of Austria
18 Belgrave Mews West, SW1X 8HU
020 7344 3250
london-ob@bmeia.gv.at
www.bmeia.gv.at/london
Monday-Friday 09.00-17.00

Cultural Section
28 Rutland Gate, SW7 1PQ
020 7225 7300
office@acflondon.org
www.acflondon.org

Defence Section
18 Belgrave Mews West, SW1X 8HU
020 7245 9185
Fax 020 7245 9185
ma.gbr@bmlvs.gv.at

Commercial Section
45 Prince's Gate, SW7 2QA
020 7584 4411
Fax 020 7584 2565
london@advantageaustria.org
www.advantageaustria.org/gb

HIS EXCELLENCY DR MICHAEL ZIMMERMANN * *Ambassador Extraordinary & Plenipotentiary (since 1 August 2018)*

Ms Katharina Kastner m *Counsellor & Deputy Head of Mission*
Mr Christoph Weingartner m *Minister Plenipotentiary (Public Diplomacy)*
Brigadier General Guenter Eisl *Attaché (Defence)*
Ms Katalin-Tuende Huber m *Director of the Austrian Cultural Forum*
Mr Christian Kesberg m *Commercial Counsellor & Trade Commissioner*
Mr Mario Gavenda *2nd Secretary (Political)*
Mr Markus Wolfsteiner m *3rd Secretary (Administrative Affairs) & Consul*
Ms Michaela Steiger m *Attaché (Administrative Affairs)*
Ms Christa Marchardt *Attaché (Cultural Affairs)*
Mr Andreas Eipeldauer *Attaché (Finance)*
Ms Vera Maier m *Attaché (Commercial)*
Ms Angelika Hable *Attaché (Police Liaison)*
Ms Bettina Kadoch *Assistant Attaché*
Ms Maria Kaefer *Assistant Attaché*
Mr Thomas Heizinger m Assistant *Attaché (Defence)*
Mr Guenter Pamminger m Assistant *Attaché (Defence)*
Ms Jasmin Lindmaier *Assistant Attaché*
Ms Paula Hack *Assistant Attaché (Cultural Affairs)*
Ms Susanne Stauder-Jentsch m, *Assistant Attaché*
Ms Jasmina Dzinic, *Assistant Attaché*

AZERBAIJAN REPUBLIC

Embassy of the Republic of Azerbaijan
4 Kensington Court W8 5DL
020 7938 3412
Fax 020 7937 1783
london@mission.mfa.gov.az
www.azembassy.org.uk
Consular Section Tel/Fax 020 7938 5482

HIS EXCELLENCY MR TAHIR TAGHIZADE m *Ambassador Extraordinary & Plenipotentiary (since 21 September 2014)*
          Mrs Ulviyya Taghizade
Mr Polad Mammadov m *1st Secretary*
Lieutenant Colonel Vugar Ahmadov m *Defence Attaché*
Mr Nijat Guliyev m *1st Secretary*
Mr Tural Ismayilov *3rd Secretary*
Mrs Gunel Salimova m *2nd Secretary*
Mr Ramin Alakbarov *2nd Secretary*

Mr Gudrat Balakishiyev **m** *Financial Attaché*
Mr Huseyn Huseynov **m** *1st Secretary*
Mr Zaur Safarov **m** *3rd Secretary*
Mr Rovshan Samadov **m** *Administrative Manager*
Mr Arif Alimammadov **m** *Administrative Manager*

BAHAMAS

High Commission of the Commonwealth of the Bahamas
10 Chesterfield Street W1J 5JL
020 7408 4488
Fax 020 7499 9937
information@bahamashclondon.net
www.bahamashclondon.net
Monday-Friday 09.30-17.30
Visa: Monday-Friday 10.00-13.00
Collection: Monday-Friday 14.00-17.30

HIS EXCELLENCY MR ELLISON EDROY GREENSLADE QPM **m** *High Commissioner (since 17 November 2017)*
        Mrs Kimberley Michelle Greenslade
Mr Marchea Alexander Mackey *3rd Secretary & Vice Consul*
Mr Anthony Arthur Stuart *Tourism Attaché*
Mrs Kimberley Michelle Greenslade **m** *Tourism Attaché*
Miss Portia Lahernia Williams *Finance Attaché*

BAHRAIN

Embassy of the Kingdom of Bahrain
30 Belgrave Square SW1X 8QB
020 7201 9170
Fax 020 7201 9183
www.bahrainembassy.co.uk
information@bahrainembassy.co.uk
Monday-Friday 09.00 -16.00

Cultural Office
98 Gloucester Road SW7 4AU
020 7341 0770
Fax 020 7373 4210
info@bcao.co.uk

HIS EXCELLENCY SHAIKH FAWAZ BIN MOHAMMED AL KHALIFA **m** *Ambassador Extraordinary & Plenipotentiary (since 1 September 2015)*
        Shaikha Buthaina Mohamed Alotaibi
Mr Hamad Waheed Mubarak Sayyar **m** *Counsellor*
Mr Tariq Khalid Mohamed **m** *Counsellor*
Mr Hasan Moosa Shafaei **m** *Counsellor*
Mr Ebrahim Abdulla Ebrahim Alshaalan **m** *First Secretary*
Mr Fahad Albinali **m** *1st Secretary*
Mr Ali A Rasool Mohamed Alalaiwat **m** *1st Secretary*
Mrs Maryam Adel Almannaei **m** *1st Secretary*
Mr Bandar Sultan Alhathal *2nd Secretary*
Mr Haitham Ragheb Altamimi **m** *3rd Secretary (Protocol)*
Mr Mohamed Khalil Nass *Attaché*
Mr Tariq Almuraikhi *Attaché*

BANGLADESH

High Commission for the People's Republic of Bangladesh
28 Queen's Gate London SW7 5JA
020 7584 0081

Fax 020 7581 7477
info@bhclondon.org.uk
www.bhclondon.org.uk
Monday-Friday 10.00-17.30
Consular Section Monday-Thursday 10.00-13.00 & delivery 15.00-16.30
Friday 10.30-12.45 & delivery 15.00-16.30

HER EXCELLENCY MS SAIDA MUNA TASNEEM **m** *High Commissioner (since 26 November 2018)*
    Mr Tauhidul I Chaudhury
Mr Muhammed Zulqar Nain **m** *Deputy High Commissioner*
Mr Shyamal Kanti Chowdhury * *Minister*
Mr Md Lutful Hasan **m** *Minister (Consular)*
Mr Ashequn Nabi Chowdhury **m** *Minister (Press)*
Mr A F M Zahid Ul Islam **m** *Minister (Political)*
Mr S M Jakaria Huq **m** *Counsellor (Commercial)*
Mr Dewan Mahmudul Haque **m** *Counsellor*
Brigadier General AKM Aminul Haque **m** *Defence Adviser*
Mr Sohel Ahmed **m** *Assistant Defence Attaché*
Mr A F M Fazle Rabbi **m** *1st Secretary (Consular)*
Mr. Md. Shafiul Alam **m** *1st Secretary (Political)*
Mr Swadipta Alam **m** *1st Secretary (Political) & HOC*
Mrs Mahfuza Sultana **m** *1st Secretary*
Mrs Mahmuda Khanam * *2nd Secretary*
Mr. Mohammad Mosaddek Hossen **m** *Attaché*

BARBADOS

Barbados High Commission
1 Great Russell Street WC1B 3ND
020 7299 7150
Fax 020 7323 6872
london@foreign.gov.bb
Monday-Friday 09.30-17.30

HIS EXCELLENCY MR MILTON ARTHUR INNISS *High Commissioner (since 17 December 2018)*
Mr Charles Merville Morris **m** *Deputy High Commissioner,*
Mr Euclid Goodman *Minister-Counsellor*
Ms Cheryl Allyson Carter *Attaché*
Ms Phyllis Small *Attaché*
Miss Sandra Yvette Forde *Attaché*
Mr Kyle Carlton Gittens *Attache*
Mrs Natasha Diane Mayers *1st Secretary*
Mr Marc Anthony Kojo McCollin *Attaché*
Mr Lennon Andrew Chandler *Attaché*

BELARUS

Embassy of the Republic of Belarus
6 Kensington Court W8 5DL
020 7937 3288
Fax 020 7938 5985
uk.london@mfa.gov.by
www.uk.mfa.gov.by
Monday-Friday 09.00-13.00 & 14.00-18.00

Economic/Commercial Section
020 7938 5988

Consular Section
020 7938 3677
uk.consul@mfa.gov.by
Monday-Friday except Wednesdays 09.00-12.30

HIS EXCELLENCY MR SERGEI ALEINIK m *Ambassador Extraordinary & Plenipotentiary (since 18 February 2013)*
      Mrs Ludmila Aleinik
Miss Larysa Belskaya *Minister-Counsellor*
Mr Dmitry Sudas m *Senior Counsellor (Economic & Commercial Affairs, Sports and Tourism)*
Mr Mikhail Metelsky *Counsellor*
Mr Aleksei Zelenko m *Counsellor (Administrative Affairs)*
Mr Pavel Kosukha m *1st Secretary (Consular, Cultural and Humanitarian Affairs)*
Col Siarhei Miechanik m *Defence Attaché (Non-Resident)*

BELGIUM

Embassy of Belgium
17 Grosvenor Crescent, SW1X 7EE
020-7470 3700
Fax: 020-7470 37
london@diplobel.fed.be
http://countries.diplomatie.belgium.be/nl/verenigd_koninkrijk
http://countries.diplomatie.belgium.be/fr/royaume_uni
http://countries.diplomatie.belgium.be/en/united_kingdom

Office of the Flemish Community and Region:
Flanders House, 1A Cavendish Square, W1G OLD
Flemish Community:
020-7299 3590
Fax: 020-7299 3591
Flanders Trade & Investment:
020-7307 7710
Fax: 020-7307 7711

HIS EXCELLENCY MR RUDOLF HUYGELEN m *Ambassador Extraordinary and Plenipotentiary (since 10 July 2017)*
      Mrs Marianne Lesceu
Mrs Ellen De Geest *Minister-Counsellor (Political Affairs)*
Captain (Naval) Renaud Flamant *Defence Attaché*
Mr Peter Verbrugghe m *Counsellor (Political Affairs)*
Mrs Sandra Kelleners *Consul General (Head of Consular and Administrative Affairs)*
Mr Laurent Preud'homme m *1st Secretary (Political & Economic Affairs)*
Mrs Agnes Scheers m *Vice Consul*
Mr. René Peeters m *Vice Consul*
Ms Sarah Grauls *2nd Secretary (Political Affairs)*
Mr André Hebbelinck *Counsellor for the Flemish Community & the Flemish Region*
Mr Jan Offner m *Economic & Commercial Counsellor for the Flemish Region*
Mr David Thonon m *Economic & Commercial Counsellor for the Walloon Region & Representative of WIB*
Mr Mohamad-Mounif Kilani m *Economic & Commercial Attaché for the Brussels Region*
Mr Nicolas Honhon m *Counsellor (Tax Expert)*
Mr Bart Brosius m *Attaché*

BELIZE

Belize High Commission
3rd Floor 45 Crawford Place W1H 4LP
020 7723 3603
info@belizehighcommission.co.uk
www.belizehighcommission.co.uk

HER EXCELLENCY MS PERLA MARIA PERDOMO *High Commissioner (since 15 July 2012)*
      Ms Carmen Scarleth Ayon Neda
Ms Karen Dawn Simplis *1st Secretary (Consular)*
Mrs Amaris Enid Leal m *1st Secretary (Political)*

BENIN

Embassy of the Republic of Benin
87 Avenue Victor Hugo 75116 Paris
00 331 45 009882
Fax 00 331 45018202
ambassade.benin@gofornet.com

London Honorary Consulate (see Honorary Consuls section below)

Vacant *Ambassador Extraordinary & Plenipotentiary*

BOLIVIA

Embassy of Bolivia
106 Eaton Square SW1W 9AD
020 7235 4248 Ext 100
Fax 020 7235 1286
embol@bolivianembassy.co.uk
www.bolivianembassy.co.uk

Consular Section
consulate@bolivianembassy.co.uk

Vacant *Ambassador Extraordinary & Plenipotentiary*
MS MARÍA JOSÉ RAQUEL OOMEN LIEBERS * *Chargé d'Affaires*

BOSNIA & HERZEGOVINA

Embassy of Bosnia & Herzegovina
5-7 Lexham Gardens W8 5JJ
020 7373 0867
020 7373 0915
Fax 020 7373 0871
embassy@bhembassy.co.uk
www.bhembassy.co.uk
Monday-Friday 09.00-17.00
Consular Section: Monday-Friday 10.00-13.00

HIS EXCELLENCY MR VANJA FILIPOVIC *Ambassador Extraordinary & Plenipotentiary (since 1 September 2019)*

Mr Igor Bašić *m* *Minister-Counsellor*
Colonel Nedžad Sadiković **m** *Military Attaché*
Ms Meliha Bašić *Counsellor (Consular Affairs)*
Ms Biljana Lučić *1st Secretary*

BOTSWANA

Botswana High Commission
6 Stratford Place W1C 1AY
020 7499 0031/020 7647 1000
Fax 020 7495 8595
bohico@govbw.com
Monday-Friday 09.00-17.00

HIS EXCELLENCY REV. DR JOHN NDEBELE G SEAKGOSING **m** *High Commissioner (since 29 December 2018)*
        Mrs Lulu Talita Seakgosing
Brig. Gabriel Addanes **m** *Defence Adviser*

Ms Faith Dimakatso Daniel *Minister-Counsellor*
Mrs Charity Lauryn Lorato Tshukudu * *Counsellor III*
Mr Johannes Kabelo Moribame *Counsellor III*
Mrs Lydia Rapelang Masole * *1st Secretary Administration*
Mr Kgomotso Abi * *Senior Commercial Attaché*
Mr Moemedi Mokgosi **m** *Commercial Attaché*
Mrs Ntshadi Gloria Galebotswe * *Education Attaché*
Ms Gloria Senabye * *Administrative Attaché*

BRAZIL

Embassy of Brazil
14/16 Cockspur Street
SW1Y 5BL
020 7747 4500
info.london@itamaraty.gov.br
http://londres.itamaraty.gov.br/en-us/

Office of the Permanent Representative to International Organisations in London
14/16 Cockspur Street, 4th floor
SW1Y 5BL
020 7747 4544 / 4548
rebraslon@itamaraty.gov.br
http://rebraslon.itamaraty.gov.br/en-us/

Consular Section
3-4 Vere Street
W1G ODH
Tel 020 76 59 1569
cg.londres@itamaraty.gov.br
http://cglondres.itamaraty.gov.br/pt-br/

Office of the Naval Adviser
170 Upper Richmond Road
SW15 2SH
020 8246 4401
Fax 020 8780 0730
www.bnce.org.uk/

Office of the Air Adviser
16 Great James Street
WC1N 3DP
020 7440 4320
Fax 020 7831 8129
cabe@bace.org.uk
https://www.bace.org.uk/

HIS EXCELLENCY MR CLAUDIO FREDERICO DE MATOS ARRUDA **m** *Ambassador Extraordinary &*
Plenipotentiary (since 8 October 2018)
        Mrs Lenice de Almeida Nóbrega Arruda
Mr Hermano Telles Ribeiro **m** *Permanent Representative to International Organisations in London*
Mr Tarcisio de Lima Ferreira Fernandes Costa **m** *Consul General*
Mr Marco Farani **m** *Permanent Representative to International Organisations in London*
Ms Ana Maria de Souza Bierrenbach *Minister-Counsellor (Multilateral)*
Mr Roberto Doring Pinho da Silva **m** *Minister-Counsellor (Deputy Head of Mission - Economic)*
Mr João Marcos Senise Paes Leme **m** *Minister-Counsellor (Deputy Head of Mission - Political)*
Mr Aloysio Marés Dias Gomide Filho **m** *Deputy Consul General*
Captain Rodrigo Otoch Chaves **m** *Defence & Naval Attaché*
Colonel André Luis Maciel de Oliveira **m** *Army Attaché*
Group Captain José Ricardo de Meneses Rocha **m** *Air Attaché*
Mr Sandro Torres Avelar **m** *Police Attaché*
Mr Augusto Luis Billi **m** *Agriculture Attaché*
Ms Mônica Maria Meirelles Nasser *Counsellor (Deputy Consul General)*

Mr Túlio Amaral Kafuri *Counsellor (Political Affairs)*
Mr Carlos Eduardo de Carvalho Pachá *Counsellor (Trade & Investment)*
Mr Otávio Augusto Drummond Cançado Trindade m *Counsellor (Political)*
Mr Rafael Souza Campos de Moraes Leme m *Counsellor (Public Diplomacy & Political)*
Mrs Leticia Frazão Alexandre de Moraes Leme m *Counsellor (Economic)*
Ms Carolina Hippolito von der Weid *1st Secretary (Agriculture & Economic)*
Ms Veridiana Lhamas de Avelar Fernandes *1st Secretary (Consul)*
Mr Lucas Nunes Beltrami *2nd Secretary (Multilateral)*
Ms Paula Rassi Brasil *2nd Secretary (Cultural)*
Mr João Eduardo Gomide de Paula m *2nd Secretary (Political)*
Mr Renato Levanteze Sant'Ana m *2nd Secretary (Multilateral)*
Mr Hugo Lins Gomes Ferreira *2nd Secretary (Consul)*
Mr Pedro Tiê Candido Souza * *2nd Secretary (Environmental)*
Mr César Linsan Passy Yip *2nd Secretary (Head of the Ambassador's office)*
Ms Carlota De Azevedo Bezerra Vitor Ramos *2nd Secretary (Education, Science & Technology)*
Ms Fernanda Carvalho Dal Piaz *2nd Secretary (Corporate Services)*
Mr Fabiano Rubio Scarano m *Vice Consul*
Mr Luiz Antonio Silva *Vice Consul*
Ms Maria Fernanda Vasconcelos de Almeida *Attaché*
Mr Francisco Carlos Leal * *Attaché*
Mr Roberto Ivens Mello de Souza * *Attaché*
Mr Luciano Gondim D'Oliveira *Vice Consul*
Mrs Helen Roberta de Souza da Conceição de Almeida m *Attaché*
Ms Maíra Moscardini de Campos *Attaché*
Mrs Renata Campos Nogueira Cid m *Vice Consul*
Mr Marcos Vinicius Gadelha Bessa m* *Attaché*
Ms Alice Amorim Campos *Vice Consul*
Mrs Janaina Gomes Fontes m *Vice Consul*
Ms Juliana Bizarria Silva *Vice Consul*
Mr Bruno de Toledo de Almeida m *Vice Consul*
Mrs Isabela Alves de Oliveira m *Vice Consul*
Mr Hugo Meirelles Júnior * *Attaché*
Mr Luiz Roberto Avelino Reciolino m *Vice Consul*
Ms Luciana Faviero de Lara Ribeiro *Attaché*
Mr Wilson Xavier da Silva *Vice Consul*
Ms Raquel Barbosa Simões *Attaché*
Mrs Marcela Malta Jucá Pimentel m *Vice Consul*
Ms Carolina Maria e Barros Silva *Vice Consul*
Captain Rogerio Moreira dos Santos m *Naval Adviser (Head of the Brazilian Naval Commission in Europe)*
Commander Flavio Leta Vieira m *Naval Adviser*
Commander Alexandre Rosa Gomes de Araujo m *Naval Adviser*
Commander Jorge Luiz Ferreira de Castro m *Naval Adviser*
Group Captain Roberto da Cunha Follador m *Air Adviser (Head of the Brazilian Aeronautical Commission in Europe)*
Captain Carlos Henrique de Lima Zampiere m *Alternate Permanent Representative to IMO*
Captain Heberth Araujo de Melo m *Alternate Permanent Representative to IMO*

BRUNEI

Brunei Darussalam High Commission
19/20 Belgrave Square SW1X 8PG
020 7581 0521
Fax 020 7235 9717
info@bruneihighcomm.org.uk

Consular Section
20 Belgrave Square SW1X 8PG
020 7581 0521 (ext. 111)
consular@bruneihighcomm.org.uk

Student Unit
35-43 Norfolk Square W2 1RX
020 7402 0045, 020 7402 0953

Fax 020 7262 8406, 020 7706 0558
Monday-Friday 09.30-13.00 & 14.00-16.30

HER EXCELLENCY PG ROOSLINA WETI PG KAMALUDIN *High Commissioner (since 31 January 2019)*

Mr Aizul Sofrin Abd Aziz * *Deputy High Commissioner*
Mr Pg Dato Yusof Sepiuddin **m** *Counsellor*
Mr Muchdieni Bin Haji Mohammad Salleh *1st Secretary*
Mrs Jihan Nabilah Dato A Rahman **m** *2nd Secretary(Political)*
Mrs Norkhalilah Roslin **m** *3rd Secretary (Admin)*
Miss Dk Hjh Nor'aidah Pg Mohd Hassan *3rd Secretary (Finance)*
Mr Anuar Hj Mahmud **m** *3rd Secretary (Protocol)*
Mr Siti Khatijah Bara **m** *3rd Secretary (Consular)*
Miss Dk Syaza Nabilah Pg Shaminan *3rd Secretary (Protocol)*
Mr Zainuddin Zainal **m** *3rd Secretary (Assistance Finance)*
Mr Khairul Amri Hj Bolhassan **m** *3rd Secretary (Finance)*
Mr Mohamad Hillman Husain *Attaché (Communication)*
Lt. Col. Mohammad Shanonnizam Sulaiman **m** *Defence Adviser*
Mr Haji Mohammad Noh Haji Tengah **m** *Defence Staff Assistant*
Mr Pg Ali Shafie Pg Hj Abas **m** *Attaché (Education)*
Mr Isham Ismail **m** *Attaché (Education)*
Mr Abdul Aziz Pandin *Attaché (Education)*
Mrs Rahimah Mohiddin *Attaché (Education)*
Mr Saidin Hidayat Abdullah Lasit **m** *Attaché (Education)*
Mrs Pg Norain Pg Ali **m** *Attaché (Education)*
Mr Khairul Sabrin Omar **m** *Attaché (Finance)*
Mr Md Anwar Mohammad *Attaché (Finance)*
Mrs Siti Norhafiza Othman **m** *Attaché (Finance)*
Ms Nur Khaliesah Othman *Attaché (Finance)*
Miss Nurulhanisah Jali *Attaché (Finance)*
Miss Hazwani Hasnan **m** *Attaché (Finance)*
Mrs Dayangku Norhayati Pengiran Luba **m** *Attaché (Finance)*
Mr Pg Haledi Pg Aliuddin **m** *Attaché (Finance)*
Mrs Norsuriaashikin Ismail **m** *Attaché (Finance)*

BULGARIA

Embassy of the Republic of Bulgaria
186-188 Queen's Gate SW7 5HL
020 7581 3144, 020 7584 9400, 020 7584 9433
Ambassador's Office 020 7591 0781
Fax 020 7584 4948
info@bulgarianembassy.org.uk
ambass.office@bulgarianembassy.org.uk
www.bulgarianembassy-london.org

Consular Section
Fax 020 7581 9073
consular@bulgarianembassy.org.uk
Monday-Friday 09.30-13.30
Individual Inquiries on Submitted Applications 13.00-15.00

Commercial Section
020 7589 4875
Fax 020 7589 4875
trade@bulgarianembassy.org.uk
Monday 10.00-16.00

HIS EXCELLENCY MR MARIN RAYKOV **m** Ambassador *Extraordinary & Plenipotentiary (since 15 May 2019)*
     Mrs Mariana Nikolova
Mrs Teofana Kraynina-Yordanova **m** *Minister Plenipotentiary Deputy Head of Mission*
Mr Andrei Vlahov **m** *Counsellor (Political Affairs)*
Mr Svetozar Dimitrov *2nd Secretary (Political Affairs & Press)*

Mrs Maria Anguelieva *Minister Plenipotentiary (Head of Consular Section)*
Mr Nikolay Vanchev **m** *Minister Plenipotentiary*
Mrs Vany Ilieva Smith **m** 1st Secretary *(Consular Section)*
Colonel Kamen Ivanov **m** *Minister Plenipotentiary (Defence Attaché)*
Mrs Tanya Koycheva **m** *Minister Plenipotentiary (Commercial Section)*
Mr Hristo Dinkov **m** *1st Secretary (Home Affairs)*
Mr Vasil Asenov *2nd Secretary (Social & Labour Affairs)*
Mr Milen Milov **m** *1st Secretary (Administrative Attaché)*
Ms Svetla Dionisieva *Counsellor (Director of the Bulgarian Cultural Institute)*

BURKINA FASO

Embassy of Burkina Faso
16 Place Guy d'Arezzo Brussels B-1180
0032 2 3459912
Fax 0032 2 3450612
contact@ambassadeduburkina.be
www.ambassadeduburkina.be
Monday-Friday 09.00-13.00 & 14.30-17.00

HER EXCELLENCY MRS JACQUELINE ZABA NIKIEMA *Ambassador Extraordinary & Plenipotentiary (since 1 August 2018)*
Mr Assane Tamboura **m** *Deputy Ambassador*
Mr Ousmane Ba **m** *1st Counsellor (Consular)*
Mr Mambila Banse **m** *Counsellor (Economic Affairs)*

BURUNDI

Embassy of the Republic of Burundi
Uganda House Second Floor 58-59 Trafalgar Square WC2N 5DX
020 7930 4958
www.burundiembassy.org.uk

HIS EXCELLENCY MR ERNEST NDABASHINZE **m** *Ambassador Extraordinary & Plenipotentiary (since 29 March 2017)*
    Mrs Gloriose Kankindi
Ms Clotilde Ntahitangira *2nd Counsellor (Economic and Social Affairs)*

CAMBODIA

Royal Embassy of Cambodia
64 Brondesbury Park Willesden Green NW6 7AT
020 8451 7997
Fax 020 8451 7594
cambodianembassy@btconnect.com
www.cambodianembassy.org.uk

Consular Section
020 8451 7850
Fax 020 8451 7594
visaenquiries@cambodianembassy.org.uk

HER EXCELLENCY DR SOEUNG RATHCHAVY **m** *Ambassador Extraordinary & Plenipotentiary (since 22 May 2017)*
    Mr Vladimir Maximov
Dr In Sopha * *Counsellor*
Mrs Sopheakleap Kong * *1st Secretary (Press & Communications)*
Mr Sovanneth Khun **m** *1st Secretary (Political)*

CAMEROON

High Commission for the Republic of Cameroon
84 Holland Park W11 3SB
020 7727 0771
Fax 020 7792 9353
Monday-Friday 09.30 - 17.30
info@cameroonhighcommission.co.uk
www.cameroonhighcommission.co.uk

HIS EXCELLENCY MR ALBERT NJOTEH FOTABONG * *High Commissioner (since 2 October 2018)*
Mrs Anna Baninla Tasha Mbur **m** *Minister Counsellor*
Mr Serge Cyrille de L'Assomption Bourne Wanmoh **m** *2nd Counsellor*
Mr Guy Elessa **m** *1st Secretary*
Mr Bonnard Carlos Tiangue Nganguen **m** *2nd Secretary*
Col Gilbert Fondufe Banka **m** *Defence Adviser*
Pr Humphrey Ngala Ndi **m** *2nd Counsellor (Cultural)*
Mr Guillaume Kimbi Loh **m** *2nd Counsellor (Communication)*
Mr Jeremie Nkoue * *2nd Counsellor (Finance)*
Mr Henri Steane Dina Imounga Mpollo **m** *1st Secretary (Communication)*
Mr Peter Ngwaya Ekema **m** *1st Secretary*
Lt-Col Gaskreo Reyang **m** *Assistant Defence Adviser*
Lt-Col Marthe Tsogo * *Naval Attaché*
Major Alain Nagmou Pene **m** *Attaché*
Captain Casimir Augustin Menye Melingui * *Attaché*

CANADA

High Commission of Canada
Canada House Trafalgar Square SW1Y 5BJ
0207 004 6000
Fax 0207 004 6050
ldn@international.gc.ca
www.UnitedKingdom.gc.ca

HER EXCELLENCY MRS JANICE CHARETTE **m** *High Commissioner (since 7 September 2016)*
        Mr Reg Charette
Ms Sarah Fountain Smith **m** *Deputy High Commissioner*
Ms Angela Gawel **m** *Minister (Migration)*
Mrs Sonya Thissen **m** *Minister-Counsellor (Political Affairs/Public Diplomacy)*
Ms Natalie Dubé *Minister-Counsellor (Commercial/Economic)*
Mr Derek Foote *Minister-Counsellor & Consul General (Management & Consular Affairs)*
Mr Stephen Wilhelm **m** *Minister-Counsellor*
Ms Claudie Senay *Counsellor*
Mr Taylor Hladik **m** *Counsellor (Commercial)*
Mr Gordon Shaffer **m** *Counsellor (Public Safety)*
Mr Robert Stevenson **m** *Counsellor (Migration)*
Ms Gillian Grant **m** *Counsellor*
Mr Ken England **m** *Counsellor*
Insp Wayne Stevenson **m** *Counsellor*
Mr Jonathan Sauvé **m** *Counsellor (Public Diplomacy)*
Mr Christopher Hough **m** *Counsellor (Defence Research & Development)*
Mr Gorav Chaudhry **m** *Counsellor (Finance)*
Mr Aaron Rosland *Counsellor (Commercial-Ontario)*
Mr Klaus Buttner **m** *Counsellor (Commercial Alberta)*
Mr Daniel Perrier *Counsellor*
Ms Shellen Liao **m** *Counsellor*
Mrs Janice Vogtle **m** *Counsellor (Economic)*
Mr Svend Holm *Counsellor*
Mr René LaMontagne **m** *Attaché (Medical)*
Mr Samir Samaha **m** *1st Secretary (Migration)*
Mr Zal Karkaria **m** *1st Secretary (Migration)*

Ms Rena Patel *1st Secretary (Migration)*
Mr Alexander Johnston *1st Secretary (Migration)*
Mr Sean Blane *1st Secretary (Management) & Consul*
Mr Craig Bell **m** *1st Secretary (CBSA)*
Mr Gene Rudyk **m** *1st Secretary (Migration)*
Mrs Karene Uzan * *1st Secretary (Migration)*
Mr Steven Owen **m** *1st Secretary (Migration)*
Ms Jennifer Jordan-Saifi **m** *1st Secretary*
Ms Julia McNeill * *1st Secretary (Management)*
Mr Michael Williams *1st Secretary*
Ms Christine Dwyer *1st Secretary (Migration)*
Ms Sarah Hall *1st Secretary (Migration)*
Mrs Suzanne Elliott * *1st Secretary*
Mrs Jennifer Wood **m** *1st Secretary*
Ms Xochipili Bryan **m** *1st Secretary (Migration)*
Mr Sean McLuckie **m** *1st Secretary (Migration)*
Mrs Laurie Blais **m** *1st Secretary (Migration)*
Ms Camille Ruest **m** *1st Secretary*
Cpl Mark Rysanek **m** *1st Secretary*
Ms Laura Lumsden *1st Secretary (Commercial)*
Mr Alain Lefebvre **m** *Attaché*
Mr Serge Seguin **m** *Attaché*
Mr Louis Vaillancourt **m** *Attaché*
Ms Sarah Hall 1st Secretary (Migration)
Mr Gurinder Singh Jande **m** *2nd Secretary*
Ms Jovonne Lee *2nd Secretary (Migration)*
Ms Leilla Cranfield *2nd Secretary*
Ms Guylaine Lasonde **m** *2nd Secretary (Migration)*
Mr Yassine Chemlal **m** *Attaché*
Sgt Joseph Benoit Mario Poulin **m** *Attaché*
Mr Michael Kachmar **m** *Attaché*

Brigadier General Michael Atkins **m** *Commander & Defence Adviser*
Colonel Andrew Lussier **m** *Army Adviser*
Colonel Paul Doyle **m** *Air Force Adviser*
Captain (N) Yves Germain **m** *Naval Adviser*
Commander Corey Bursey **m** *Assistant Naval Adviser*
Lieutenant-Colonel James Price **m** *Assistant Army Adviser*
Lieutenant-Colonel Pierre Theriault **m** *Assistant Air Force Adviser*

Commander Mitchell de Savoye **m** *Attaché*
Major Gregory Pappoulas **m** *Attaché*
Captain Della Boucher *Attaché*
PO1 Daniel Hyland **m** *Attaché*

CABO VERDE

Embassy of the Republic of Cabo Verde
Avenue Jeane 29 1050 Brussels
0032 2643 6270
Fax 0032 2646 3385
emb.caboverde@skynet.be

London Honorary Consulate (see Honorary Consuls section below)

Vacant *Ambassador Extraordinary & Plenipotentiary*
Mr Octavio Bento Gomes **m** *Counsellor, Chargé d'Affaires a.i*
Ms Dulce Helena Barbosa Vicente Silver Fernandes *Counsellor*
Ms Sonia Maria Lizardo Andrade *1st Secretary*

CENTRAL AFRICAN REPUBLIC

Embassy of the Central African Republic
30 Rue des Perchamps 75016 Paris

Vacant *Ambassador Extraordinary & Plenipotentiary*

CHAD

Embassy of the Republic of Chad
Boulevard Lambermont 52 1030 Brussels
0032 2215 1975
Fax 0032 2216 3526
ambassade.tchad@chello.be

HIS EXCELLENCY Mr OUSMANE MATAR BREME **m** *Ambassador Extraordinary & Plenipotentiary (since 06 January 2015)*
        Halime Mahamat Moukhtar
Mr Beadrone Nagarbaye Tombalaye *Chargé d'Affaires*
Mr Ahmat Issaka Diar *Minister-Counsellor*
Mr Detomal Nahogoum *Counsellor (Economic)*
Mr Bakhit Mahamat Saleh Brahim *1st Secretary*
Mr Hissein Abdoulaye Hartaka *Attaché*
Mr Mahamat Djourab Mallaye *Attaché (Press)*

CHILE

Embassy of Chile
37-41 Old Queen Street SW1H 9JA
020 7222 2361
Fax 020 7222 0861
embachile@embachile.co.uk
http://chile.gob.cl/reino-unido/es/

Consulate General
37-41 Old Queen Street SW1H 9JA
020 7222 2361
http://chile.gob.cl/londres/es/

Commercial Office
37-41 Old Queen Street SW1H 9JA
020 7233 2500
Fax 020 7233 2501
info@prochile.co.uk
www.prochile.co.uk

Defence & Naval Attaché's Office
37-41 Old Queen Street SW1H 9JA
020 7292 1500/02
Fax 020 7434 0793

Military Attaché's Office
37-41 Old Queen Street SW1H 9JA
020 7233 3851

Air Attaché's Office
37-41 Old Queen Street SW1H 9JA
020 7799 5442
Fax 020 7222 3607

Carabineros Attaché's Office
37-41 Old Queen Street SW1H 9JA
020 7222 2361

Civil Police Attaché's Office
37-41 Old Queen Street SW1H 9JA
020 7222 2361

Office of the Alternate Permanent Representative to the IMO
37-41 Old Queen Street SW1H 9JA
020 7222 2361

HIS EXCELLENCY MR DAVID GALLAGHER m *Ambassador Extraordinary & Plenipotentiary and Permanent Representative of Chile to the IMO (since 3 August 2018)*
      Mrs Sara Crespo Ureta
Mr Julio Alejandro Méndez Olave m *Minister Counsellor & Deputy Head of Mission*
Mr Jaime Muñoz m *Counsellor & Consul General*
Mr Ignacio Fernández m *Commercial Attaché*
Captain Daniel Alejandro Munoz Miranda m *Defence Attaché*
Colonel Sergio Gutierrez m *Military Attaché*
Group Captain Milton Zablah m *Air Attaché*
Colonel Carlos Abarza *Police Attaché*
Captain Jose Miguel Hernandez Jacir m *Naval Attaché*
Captain Nelson Saavedra m *Alternate Permanent Representative to IMO*
Mrs Karina Jane Concha m *2nd Secretary*
Mr Francisco Tello *2nd Secretary (Consul)*
Mr Pablo Andres Ibarra Cordero m *Civil Police Attaché*
Lieutenant Commander Ignacio Ortiz m *Alternate Permanent Representative to IMO*

CHINA

Embassy of the People's Republic of China
49-51 Portland Place W1B 1JL
020 7299 4049
Monday-Friday 09.00-12.30, 14.00-17.00
www.chinese-embassy.org.uk

Political Section
49-51 Portland Place W1B 1JL
020 7299 4055

Policy and Research Section
49-51 Portland Place W1B 1JL
020 7299 4074

Press and Public Affairs Section
49-51 Portland Place W1B 1JL
020 7299 4088

Administration Section
49-51 Portland Place W1B 1JL
020 7299 4021

Consular Section
31 Portland Place W1B 1QD
020 7631 1430

Defence Section
25 Lyndhurst Road NW3 5PA
020 7794 7595

Commercial Section
16 Lancastar Gate W2 3LH
020 7087 4949

Cultural Section
11 West Heath Road NW3 7UX
020 7431 8830

Education Section
50 Portland Place W1B 1NQ
020 7612 0260

Science & Technology Section
10 Greville Place NW6 5JN
020 7625 0079

Maritime Section
31 Portland Place W1B 1QD
020 7299 8439

HIS EXCELLENCY MR LIU XIAOMING **m** Ambassador Extraordinary & Plenipotentiary (since 28 February 2010)
    Mme Hu Pinghua
Mr Ma Hui **m** *Minister*
Mr Guo Yuliang * *Minister-Counsellor*
Mr Yang Xiaokun * *Minister-Counsellor*
Mr Qi Wang * **m** Minister-Counsellor
Mrs Chen Wen * *Minister-Counsellor*
Mr Jin Xu **m** *Minister-Counsellor* (Commercial Section)
Mr Bin Zhu * *First Secretary - Commercial*
Mr WANG Yongli * *Minister-Counsellor* (Education Section)
Mr Peng Yu **m** *Minister-Counsellor* (Cultural Section)
Mr Jiang Sunan **m** *Minister-Counsellor* (Science & Technology Section)
Major General Su Guanghui **m** *Defence Attaché* (Defence Section)
Mr Fei Mingxing **m** *Minister-Counsellor* (Consular Section)
Mr Hongwei Wang **m** *Counsellor* (Policy and Research Section)
Mrs Zeng Rong **m** *Counsellor* (Press and Public Affairs Section)
Mr Pan Zhengmao **m** *Counsellor* (Administration Office)
Miss Yuzi Xia *Minister Counsellor* (Administration Office)
Mr Guo Chentao * *Counsellor* (Policy and Research Section)
Mr Zhang Limin **m** *Counsellor* (Political Section)
Mr Lu Haitian * *Counsellor* (Consular Section)
Mr Zhao Guohua **m** *Counsellor* (Political Section)
Mr Yang Ruiguang **m** *Counsellor* (Political Section)
Mr Shao Zheng **m** *Counsellor* (Policy and Research Section)
Mr Li Gang **m** *Counsellor* (Policy and Research Section)
Mr Zhang Xuesong * *Counsellor* (Political Section)
Mr Wei Sun **m** *Counsellor* (Press and Public Affairs)
Mr Mi Yang **m** *Counsellor* (Commercial Section)
Mr Xia Jianhui * *Counsellor* (Education Section)
Mr Xin Ma **m** *Counsellor* (Political Section)
Mrs Li Jiangning **m** *1st Secretary* (Political Section)
Mr Pan Feiya **m** *1st Secretary* (Political Section)
Mrs Wang Xiaojing * *1st Secretary* (Political Section)
Mrs Zhang Chi * *2nd Secretary* (Political Section)
Mr Dang Xinkai **m** *2nd Secretary* (Political Section)
Ms Yang Nan * *3rd Secretary* (Political Section)
Mr Zhao Yong * *3rd Secretary* (Political Section)
Mrs Xiaorui Wu **m** *3rd Secretary* (Political Section)
Mrs Wang Limian **m** *Attaché* (Political Section)
Ms Zhong Hua * *Attaché* (Political Section)
Mr Wei Ye *Attache (Political Section)*
Mr Feng Jialiang **m** *1st Secretary* (Policy and Research Section)
Mr Xiang Wei * *2nd Secretary* (Policy and Research Section)
Mr Cheng Xu **m** *2nd Secretary* (Policy and Research Section)
Mr Li Jiandong * *3rd Secretary* (Policy and Research Section)
Mr Liu Cheng **m** *3rd Secretary* (Policy and Research Section)
Mr Qiu Ji * *Attaché* (Policy and Research Section)
Ms Long Jingni * *Attaché* (Policy and Research Section)
Mr Rui Li * *Attache* (Political Section)
Mr Dingkun Zhu **m** *Attaché* (Administration Section)
Mr Yi Yang * *Attache* (Political Section)

Mr Yan Bo Wang m *2nd Secretary* (Press and Public Affairs Section)
Mr Qiu Ke * *1st Secretary* (Press and Public Affairs Section)
Mrs Zheng Shouhui * *2nd Secretary* (Press and Public Affairs Section)
Mr Ren Chao m *3rd Secretary* (Press and Public Affairs Section)
Mr Zhang Xiaodong m *1st Secretary* (Maritime Section)
Mr Li Tao * *1st Secretary* (Maritime Section)
Mrs Chen Wen * *1st Secretary* (Administration Office)
Mr Chen Jianping m *1st Secretary* (Administration Office)
Mrs Li Wenjun m *2nd Secretary* (Administration Office)
Mr Zhao Guanghui m *2nd Secretary* (Administration Office)
Mr Wei Chen *3rd Secretary* (Administration Office)
Mrs Li Jiahang * *3rd Secretary* (Administration Office)
Mr Wang Fei m *3rd Secretary* (Administration Office)
Mr Qiu Ersheng m *3rd Secretary* (Administration Office)
Mrs Fu Jingxin m *3rd Secretary* (Administration Office)
Mrs Rui Xu m *3rd Secretary* (Administration Office)
Mrs Li Honghua * *Attaché* (Administration Office)
Mrs Ting Chen m *Attaché* (Administration Office)
Mr Wang Dayin m *1st Secretary* (Administration Office)
Mr Wei Xuehui * *1st Secretary* (Administration Office)
Mrs Liu Ying * *1st Secretary* (Administration Office)
Mr Du Jitao m *2nd Secretary* (Consular Section)
Mr Wang Xiaowei m *1st Secretary* (Consular Section)
Mr Han Jianwei * *1st Secretary* (Consular Section)
Mrs Zhang Ying m *1st Secretary* (Consular Section)
Mr Pengfie Xiong *Attaché* (Consular Section)
Mrs Lyu Chunju m 3rd Secretary (Consular Section)
Mrs Zhang Qiong * *2nd Secretary* (Consular Section)
Mrs Qu Yan * *1st Secretary* (Consular Section)
Mrs Xujiao Yan * *2nd Secretary* (Consular Section)
Senior Colonel Chen Jun m *Army Attaché* (Defence Section)
Senior Group Captain Dai Jinhua * *Air Attaché* (Defence Section)
Captain (Navy) Zhang Yanbo m *Navy Attaché* (Defence Section)
Mr Feng Gao m *Deputy Defence Attaché* (Defence Section)
Lieutenant Colonel Liu Jun m *Deputy Defence Attaché* (Defence Section)
Colonel Xu Sheng m *Deputy Defence Attaché* (Defence Section)
Lieutenant Colonel Tang Xiao m *Assistant to Defence Attaché* (Defence Section)
Mrs Zhao Wanming * *1st Secretary* (Commercial Section)
Mr Huang Hongyong m *1st Secretary* (Commercial Section)
Mr Zheng Jiang m *1st Secretary* (Commercial Section)
Mrs Xi An * *1st Secretary* (Commercial Section)
Mrs Hou Le * *2nd Secretary* (Commercial Section)
Ms Na Liu *1st Secretary* (Commercial Section)
Mr Wang Zheng m *3rd Secretary* (Commercial Section)
Mr Zhiqiang Gao m *1st Secretary* (Commercial Section)
Mr Chun Wang m *2nd Secretary* (Commercial Section)
Ms Yi Zihan * *Attaché* (Commercial Section)
Mr Sun Chao * *1st Secretary* (Cultural Section)
Mr Zhao Xu m *2nd Secretary* (Culture Section)
Mr Yu Guo * *2nd Secretary* (Cultural Section)
Mrs Ma Lei m *2nd Secretary* (Cultural Section)
Ms Mo Xia * *Attaché* (Cultural Section)
Mr Wang Zeyu m *1st Secretary* (Education Section)
Mr Shi Lei m *1st Secretary* (Education Section)
Mrs Ting Wang m *2nd Secretary* (Education Section)
Mr Guoqiang Li m *1st Secretary* (Education Section)
Ms Yu Haiying * *2nd Secretary* (Education Section)
Mr Song Shi m *1st Secretary* (Education Section)
Mr Zheng Wang m *2nd Secretary* (Education Section)
Mrs Ruan Shao * *3rd Secretary* (Education Section)
Mr Tan Ge m *1st Secretary* (Science & Technology Section)
Mrs Wang Jing m *1st Secretary* (Science & Technology Section)
Mr Tan Junyao m *2nd Secretary* (Science & Technology Section)
Mrs Ma Huiqin * *2nd Secretary* (Science & Technology Section)

Mr Wenqing Li m 2nd Secretary (Economic & Commercial)
Mrs Xiangxin Cui m *2nd Secretary* (Economic & Commercial)
Mr He Huang m *First Secretary* (Science & Technology Section)
Mrs Huiping Xie m *First Secretary* (Science & Technology Section)

COLOMBIA

Embassy of Colombia
3 Hans Crescent SW1X 0LN
020 7589 9177 / 020 7589 5037
Fax 020 7581 1829
elondres@cancilleria.gov.co
http://granbretana.embajada.gov.co

Consulate General
Ground and 3rd Floor, 35 Portland Place, London W1B 1AE
020 7637 9893 / 020 7927 7121
Fax 020 7637 5604
clondres@cancilleria.gov.co
http://londres.consulado.gov.co

Commercial Office
ProColombia
6th Floor, 2 Conduit Street, London W1S 2XB
020 7491 3535
Fax 020 7491 4295
london@procolombia.co

Military, Naval & Police Attaché's Office
3rd Floor, 83 Victoria Street, London SW1H 0HW
020 3170 6012 / 075 9018 8269

HIS EXCELLENCY MR ANTONIO JOSÉ ARDILA m *Ambassador Extraordinary & Plenipotentiary (Since 8 March 2019)*
      Mrs Luz Angela Sarmiento Gutiérrez
Mr Vicente Fernando Echandia-Roldan *Deputy Head of Mission*
Ms Maria Ximena Duran-Sanin *Consul General*
Mr Jose Ricardo Puyana-Valdivieso m *Commercial Attaché*
Mr Jaime Alberto Mejia-Alvaran m *Counsellor*
Mrs Maria del Pilar Mira-Ponton m *Cultural Attaché - 2nd Secretary*
Mr Jaime Andres Diaz-Silva *3rd Secretary*
Mr Miguel Felipe Castiblanco-Monsalve *Vice Consul – 2nd Secretary*
Miss Natasha Arroyave-Monsalve *Vice Consul – 2nd Secretary*
Captain Gilberto Antonio Sanchez-Angulo m *Permanent Representative to IMO*
Captain William Fernando Carvajal-Fierro m *Naval Attaché*
Colonel Jorge Hernando Morales-Villamizar m *Police Attaché*
Colonel Gabriel Espinosa-Botia m *Military & Air Attaché*
Colonel Jose Manuel Gomez-Valenzuela m *Deputy Military & Air Attaché*

CONGO

Embassy of the Republic of Congo
37 bis Rue Paul Valéry 75116 Paris, France
0033 1 4500 6057
Fax 0033 1 4067 1733

London Honorary Consulate (see Honorary Consuls section below)

Vacant *Ambassador Extraordinary & Plenipotentiary*

CONGO (DEMOCRATIC REPUBLIC)

Embassy of the Democratic Republic of the Congo
45-49 Great Portland Street W1W 7LD
020 7580 3931
Fax 020 7580 8713
missionrdclondres@gmail.com
info@ambardc-londres.gouv.cd
www.ambardc-londres.gouv.cd
Monday,Wednesday and Friday 09:30-12:00 Visa Submissions
Wednesay & Friday 12:00-13:00 Visa Collections

Documentation & Cultural Resource Bureau(DCRB)
281 Gray's Inn Road,
London WC1X 8QF
Tuesdays 9:30-17:30 except on public holidays.
Identification and Biometric Data Collection for Congolese Nationals:
Tuesday 10:00-17:00

HER EXCELLENCY MS MARIE NDJEKA OPOMBO *Ambassador Extraordinary & Plenipotentiary (since 20 February 2017)*
Mr Eric Mulume Oderhwa Migabo **m** *1st Counsellor*
Mr Napo Ghonda Mbe Lukuya Ntela * *Minister-Counsellor*
Mr Hyppolite Olamba Ossomba * *2nd Counsellor*
Mrs Fanny Kayaya Beya * *2nd Secretary*
Mr Phinees Kabango Muepu **m** *Political Attaché*
Mr Fabrice Boluwa Londole * *Alternate Permanent Representative of the DRC to the IMO*

COSTA RICA

Embassy of Costa Rica
23 Woodstock Street W1C 2AS
info@costaricanembassy.co.uk
Monday-Friday 10.00-17.00

Consular Section
23 Woodstock Street W1C 2AS
consul@costaricanembassy.co.uk

HIS EXCELLENCY MR RAFAEL ORTIZ FÁBREGA **m** *Ambassador Extraordinary & Plenipotentiary (since 31 October 2018)*
          Mrs Laura Valverde Borbón
Mr Jorge Arturo Aguilar Castillo * *Minister Counsellor & Consul General*
Mr Francisco Jose Masís Holdridge * *Counsellor & Consul General*

CÔTE D'IVOIRE

Embassy of the Republic of Côte d'Ivoire
2 Upper Belgrave Street SW1X 8BJ
020 7235 6991
Fax 0207 259 5320
TELEX 23906 Ivory Coast
Monday-Friday 09.30-13.00 & 14.00-17.00

Consular Section
2 Upper Belgrave Street SW1X 8BJ

Commercial & Economic Section (Commodities)
Morley House 3rd Floor 314-322 Regent Street W1B 3BE
020 7462 0086
Fax 020 7462 0087

HIS EXCELLENCY MR GEORGES ABOUA **m** *Ambassador Extraordinary & Plenipotentiary (since 23 October 2015)*
        Mrs Nee Seriba Christiane Aboua
Mrs Salome Vanie **m** *1st Counsellor*
Mr Aly Toure **m** *Counsellor (International Organisations Section Commodities)*
Mr Diomande Gondo Serge Siaba **m** *Counsellor (Economic)*
Mr Euloge Innocent Atse **m** *Counsellor (International Organisations)*
Mr David Jacques Mimran **m** *Counsellor (Economic)*
Mr Diagne Mamadou N'Diaye **m** *Counsellor (Commercial)*
Mr Gadji Rabe **m** *Counsellor (Consular Affairs)*
Mrs Roselyne Salomé Vanié Nee Bede **m** *Counsellor*
Mr Dramane Kone **m** *Financial Counsellor*
Mr Mory Diarrassounba **m** *Counsellor (Commercial)*
Mr Adou Herve Stanislas **m** *1ˢᵗ Secretary (Tourism)*
Mrs Kouablan Marie Mea *Counsellor*

CROATIA

Embassy of the Republic of Croatia
21 Conway Street W1T 6BN
020 7387 2022
Fax 020 7387 0310
vrhlon@mvep.hr
http://uk.mvp.hr
Monday-Friday 09.00-17.00

Consular Section
21 Conway Street W1T 6BN
Fax 020 7387 0936
conlon@mvep.hr

Mr Igor Pokaz **m** *Ambassador Extraordinary and Plenipotentiary*
Colonel Damir Terzić **m** *Defence Attaché*
Mr Domagoj Rogulj *Counsellor, Political Affairs*
Mr Tomislav Vlahutin **m** *First Secretary (Economic and Cultural Affairs)*
Ms Nelija Vržina **m** *First Secretary (Political Affairs)*
Ms Iva Gudelj *First Secretary (Consular Affairs)*

CUBA

Embassy of the Republic of Cuba
167 High Holborn WC1V 6PA
020 7240 2488
Fax 020 7836 2602
secembajador@uk.embacuba.cu
www.cubadiplomatica.cu

Consular Section
167 High Holborn WC1V 6PA
020 7240 2488
Fax 020 7379 4557

HER EXCELLENCY MRS TERESITA DE JESÚS VICENTE SOTOLONGO **m** *Ambassador Extraordinary & Plenipotentiary*
        Mr Antonio Rogelio Rodríguez Valcárcel
Mr Antonio Rogelio Rodríguez Valcárcel **m** *(Minister-Counsellor)*
Mr Julio Enrique Pujol Torres **m** *Counsellor (Political Affairs)*
Mrs Olena Estela Navas Pérez **m** *Counsellor (Economic Affairs)*
Mr Joel Hernández González **m** *Counsellor (Tourism Affairs)*
Mrs Lidice Caridad Veguería López **m** *Counsellor (Consular Affairs)*
Mr Aristides Julian Hechavarria Torrijo **m** *Counsellor (Press and Cultural Affairs)*
Mr Roberto Ricardo de la Peña Pino **m** *Attaché*

Mr Julian Alexis Ávila Velázquez m *Attaché*

CYPRUS

High Commission of the Republic of Cyprus
13 St. James's Square SW1Y 4LB
020 7321 4100
Fax 020 7321 4164
CyprusinUK@mfa.gov.cy
www.cyprusinuk.com
Monday-Friday 09:00-16:30
Consular Section, Monday-Friday 09:30-13:00

High Commissioner's Private Secretary
020 7321 4101
Fax 020 7321 4162
CyprusHCLondon@mfa.gov.cy

Political Section
020 7321 4126
Fax 020 7321 4164
CyprusinUK@mfa.gov.cy

Consular Section
020 7321 4100
Fax 020 7321 4160
hclconsular@mfa.gov.cy
For Medical and Sponsored Patients issues
hclmedical@mfa.gov.cy

Maritime Section
020 7321 4154
Fax 020 7321 4171
dmslondon@dms.gov.cy

Commercial Section
020 7321 4141
Fax 020 7321 4169
info@cyprustrade.co.uk

Tourism Section
020 7321 4170
londonadmincto@btconnect.com

Cultural Section
020 7321 4148
Fax 020 7321 4164

Press Section
020 7321 4127
Fax 020 7321 4164
hclpress@mfa.gov.cy

Cyprus Educational Mission
020 8881 6982
Fax 020 8365 8257
kea@schools.ac.cy

HIS EXCELLENCY MR ANDREAS S KAKOURIS **m** High *Commissioner* (since 01 September 2019)
    Mrs Kareen Farrell-Kakouris
Mr Nicholaos T Manolis **m** *Deputy High Commissioner*
Mr Andreas Eliades **m** *Counsellor*
Mr Theodoros Gkotsis *Consul General*

Col Eleftherios Hadjistefanou * *Defence Attaché*
Mr Marios Stephanides *Counsellor (Maritime Affairs)*
Mr Marios Psaras *Cultural Counsellor*
Ms Emelia-Stella Christodoulidou *Attaché (Communications, Security and Labour Affairs)*

CZECH REPUBLIC

Embassy of the Czech Republic
26-30 Kensington Palace Gardens W8 4QY
020 7243 1115
london@embassy.mzv.cz
consulate.london@embassy.mzv.cz
Fax : 020 7243 7926
www.mzv.cz/london

HIS EXCELLENCY MR LIBOR SECKA **m** *Ambassador Extraordinary & Plenipotentiary (since 5 January 2016)*
        Mrs Sabrina Seckova
Mr Jan Brunner **m** *Minister-Counsellor & Deputy Head of Mission*
Colonel Jiri Niedoba * *Defence Attaché*
Ms Marketa Sterbova * *1st Secretary (Political Affairs)*
Ms Marketa Hajkova * *3rd Secretary (Political Affairs)*
Mr Ales Opatrny **m** *3rd Secretary (Head of Economic & Commercial Affairs)*
Ms Jana Cechlovska * *3rd Secretary (Political Affairs)*
Mrs Alice Navratilova **m** *1st* Secretary (Consular Affairs)
Mr Simona Padourkova **m** *1st Secretary (Consular Affairs)*
Miss Tereza Porybna * *2nd Secretary (Director of the Czech Centre)*
Mr Martin Pluhar *3rd Secretary (Head of Administration)*
Mr Ondrej Hovadek * *3rd Secretary*
Mr Filip Jiri * *Attaché*
Mr Tomas Dokulil **m** *Attaché*

DENMARK

Royal Danish Embassy
55 Sloane Street SW1X 9SR
020 7333 0200
Fax 020 7333 0270
lonamb@um.dk
www.storbritannien.um.dk
Monday-Thursday 09.00-16.30 & Friday 09.00-16.00

Consular Section
Monday-Friday: By appointment only
Passports 020 7333 0200
Visas 020 7333 0200
Fax 020 7333 0266

Defence Attaché's Office
020 7333 0228/0229
Fax 020 7333 0231

Representation of the Faroes
Tel. 020 7333 0227/0207
Fax 020 7333 6707
info@tinganes.fo
www.faroes.org.uk

HIS EXCELLENCY MR LARS THUESEN **m** *Ambassador Extraordinary & Plenipotentiary (since 01 September 2017)*
        Mrs Jeanine Arreguin Ayerdi
Mr Ulrik Enemark Petersen * *Minister-Counsellor & Deputy Head of Mission*
Mr Allan Stagaard Toft *Counsellor (European Policy and Financial Affairs)*

Mr Uffe Grøn-Søresen **m** *Counsellor (Political)*
Mrs Mette Diego-Roll **m** *Counsellor (Commercial Affairs)*
Mr Jacob Byskov Kristensen **m** *Policy Advisor (Energy)*
Mr Dennis Blicher * *Consul*
Brigadier General Lars Christian Hedemark **m** *Defence Attaché*
Pastor Mr Flemming Kloster Poulsen **m** *Attaché (Social Affairs)*
Mr Áki Johansen **m** *Minister-Counsellor (Representative of the Government of the Faroes)*

DJIBOUTI

Embassy of the Republic of Djibouti
26 Rue Emile Ménier 75116 Paris
0033 1 4727 4922
Fax 0033 1 4553 5053
webmaster@amb-djibouti.org
www.ambdjibouti.org

HIS EXCELLENCY MR AYEID MOUSSEID YAHYA **m** *Ambassador Extraordinary & Plenipotentiary (since 22 January 2015)*
        Mrs Manuelle Calligny

DOMINICA, COMMONWEALTH OF

Office of the High Commissioner for the Commonwealth of Dominica
1 Collingham Gardens SW5 0HW
020 7370 5194
Fax 020 7373 8743
info@dominicahighcommission.co.uk
www.dominicahighcommission.co.uk
Monday-Friday 09.30-17.30

Vacant *High Commissioner*

Mrs Janet Charles **m** *Acting High Commissioner & 2nd Secretary*
Ms Nakinda Daniel *3rd Secretary*

DOMINICAN REPUBLIC

Embassy of the Dominican Republic
81 Cromwell Road, SW7 5BW
020 7262 6856
pa@dominicanembassy.org.uk
www.dominicanembassy.org.uk
Monday-Friday 10.00-16.00
Consular Section
consulate@dominicanembassy.org.uk

HIS EXCELLENCY MR HUGO MAXIMILIANO GUILIANI CURY *Ambassador Extraordinary & Plenipotentiary (since 4 February 2019)*

Mr Francisco Manuel Comprés Hernández *Minister-Counsellor, Deputy Head of Mission*
Mr Jose Tomas Perez Gautreau **m** *Minister-Counsellor (Cultural Affairs)*
Mrs Marlen Vásquez **m** *Minister-Counsellor (Cooperation & Cultural Affairs)*
Mr Gustavo Adolfo Sosa Ricardo *Minister-Counsellor (Political Affairs)*
Miss Nicole Jacobo *Counsellor (Trade, Investment & Political Affairs)*
Mr Joan Jose Monegro Medina *Counsellor (Economic & Consular Affairs)*
Mr Joan Alemany Nunez *Counsellor (Financial & Administrative Affairs)*

ECUADOR

Embassy of Ecuador
Flat 3b 3 Hans Crescent SW1X 0LS
020 7584 1367 / 020 7590 2501 / 020 7590 2507
eecugbr@cancilleria.gob.ec
website: http://www.reinounido.embajada.gob.ec

Consular Section
9 John Sessions Square E1 8NQ
020 7451 0040 / 0207 278 2923
Fax 020 3503 0991
ceculdn@cancilleria.gob.ec
website: http://www.londres.consulado.gob.ec

Defence Attaché's Office and Permanent Representative to the IMO
Flat 4, 5 Lawson Close, Wimbledon, London, SW19 5EL
020 8715 3594
agderu@armada.mil.ec

Commercial Section
Institute for Export and Investment
5th Floor, 141-142 Fenchurch Street, London EC3M 6BL
020 3078 8042 / 0203 078 8045
london@proecuador.gob.ec

HIS EXCELLENCY MR JAIME ALBERTO MARCHAN-ROMERO m *Ambassador Extraordinary & Plenipotentiary*
(since 17 December 2018)
      Mrs Maria Del Rocio Barahona-Riera
Mr Leopoldo Enrique Rovayo-Verdesoto m *Minister*
Captain Gabriel Armando Abad Neuner m *Defence Attaché & Alternate Representative to the IMO*
Mr Francisco Javier Llorca Vega m *Counsellor*
Mr Juan Carlos Yépez *Commercial Counsellor*
Mr Pablo Andres Roldan Ribadeneira m *2nd Secretary - Consul*
Mrs Carolina Jacqueline Troya Palacios m *2nd Secretary (Trade Officer)*
Miss Ana Cristina Albonoz Flores *2nd Secretary (Trade Officer)*
Mr Bolivar Urquizo Tenesaca m *3rd Secretary*
Mrs Cynthia Del Carmen Aleman Yepez m *Cultural & Education Attaché*
Ms Maritza Del Rocio Arauz Castro *Administrative Attaché*

EGYPT

Embassy of the Arab Republic of Egypt
26 South Street, W1K 1DW
Tel.: 020 7499 3304/2401
Fax: 020 7491 1542
E-mail address: egtamboff@gmail.com
                egyemblondon@mfa.gov.eg
Opening Hours: Monday-Friday 9:00-17:00

Consulate General
Visas, Legalisations, Egyptian Nationals
2 Lowndes Street, SW1X 9ET
Tel: 020 7235 9719
Fax: 020 7235 5684
E-mail: info@egyptconsulate.co.uk

Defence Office:
24 South Street, W1K 1DN
Tel: 020 7493 2649
Fax: 020 7495 3573
E-mail: egyptiandefenseoffice.uk@gmail.com

Commercial Office:
23 South Street, W1K 2XD

Tel: 020 7499 3002
Fax: 020 7493 8110
E-mail: london@ecs.gov.eg

Medical Office:
47 Longridge Road, SW5 9SD
Tel: 020 7370 6944
Fax: 020 7370 36
E-mail: amrabdelhady@egmedoffice.org

Press & Information Office
299 Oxford Street, W1C 2DZ
Tel: 020 7409 2236
Fax: 020 7493 7456
E-mail: info@egpressoffice.com

Cultural Office:
4 Chesterfield Gardens, W1J 5BG
Tel: 020 7491 7720
Fax: 020 7408 1335
E-mail: administration@egyptcultue.org.uk

State Tourist Bureau:
170 Piccadilly, W1J 9EJ
Tel: 020 7493 5283
Fax: 020 7408 0295
E-mail: info@gotoegypt.org

HIS EXCELLENCY MR TAREK AHMED IBRAHIM ADEL Ambassador Extraordinary and Plenipotentiary (Since 22nd November 2018)
　　　　Mrs. Mona Mohamed Salah Eldin Said
Mrs Nermine M.E.E. ElZawahry, Minister Plenipotentiary *Deputy Chief of Mission*
Dr Hany A. Khedr Mohamed *Counsellor*
Mr Ibrahim M.A.I Salem **m** *Counsellor*
Mrs Marwa A.A. Youssef **m** *Counsellor*
Mr Ahmed E. M. Ahmed * *Counsellor*
Mr Mohamed K.A.A. Amer * *Counsellor*
Mr Sherif A.S.I. Eissa **m** *1st Secretary*
Ms Reem M. A. Eldahshan *2nd Secretary*
Ms Asmaa S.M. Zayed *3rd Secretary*
Mr Tarek F.A. Youssef **m** *Consul General*
Mr Ahmed A. Hamadnalla Ibrahim **m** *Consul*
Mr Walid O.K.Ali * *Consul*
Brig. General Hisham A. E. Sultan **m** *Defence Attaché*
Col. Dr. Ahmed M.A. Ziada **m** *Assistant Defence Attaché*
Col. Mohamed I.F.A. ElMesslawi **m** *Assistant Defence Attaché*
Col. Medhat S.A.Helal **m** *Assistant Defence Attaché*
Col.Tamer M.E.Nabhan **m** *Assistant Defence Attaché*
Lt. Col Ahmed M.I. Heikal **m** *Assistant Defence Attaché*
Major Moataz M.A.M.E.Salama **m** *Assistant Defence Attaché*
Major Pilot Mohamed R.G.A.Mohamed **m** *Assistant Defence Attaché*
Prof. Dr. Reem M.R.B. Abdelmotaal *Cultural Counsellor*
Mr Mohamed H. Bassiuny **m** *Minister Plenipotentiary (Commercial)*
Mr Kareem Abdallah **m** *1st Secretary (Commercial)*
Mrs Manal A.R. Elshabrawy **m** *Counsellor (Press & Information)*
Mr Amr A. Elezabi **m** *Counsellor (Tourism & Information)*
Prof. Amr. M.A. Sharaf **m** *Counsellor (Medical Office)*
Mr Ibrahim F. Mohieldeen * Minister Plenipotentiary, *Head of League of Arab States*
Mrs Riham Medhat Mohamed Samy **m** *Administrative Attaché'& Information Office*
Mr Nasser A. A. Elhosseiny **m** *Administrative & Financial Attaché'*
Mr Adel M. B. Khairy *Administrative & Financial Attaché*
Mr Ahmed A.A. Awad **m** *Administrative & Financial Attaché*
Mrs Hadir F.M.F. Elgendy **m** *Administrative & Financial Attaché*

Mr Aly Salem **m** *Administrative & Financial Attaché'*
Mr Mohamed A. A. Mahmoud **m** *Administrative & Financial Attaché'*
Mr Ashraf A. M. Badraa * *Administrative & Financial Attaché*
Mr Ahmed M.A.Abdellatif **m** *Administrative & Financial Attaché*
Mrs Nadia A. M. Badawi * *Administrative & Financial Attaché*
Mrs Soheir M. A. Ragab **m** *Administrative & Financial Attaché (Consulate)*
Mr Yousri A. K. Hozayen **m** *Administrative & Financial Attaché (Consulate)*
Mrs. Eman T. A. Khafagey **m** *Administrative & Financial Attaché (Consulate)*
Mrs. Dina Atef M. Ibrahim **m** *Administrative & Financial Attaché (Consulate)*
Mr. Ahmed Adel A. Tawfik **m** *Administrative & Financial Attaché (Consulate)*
Ms Marwa S. A. Ammar *Administrative & Financial Attaché (Consulate)*
Mr. Said M. S. Elhamzawy **m** *Administrative & Financial Attaché (Consulate)*
Mr. Hussein S. H. Ahmed * *Administrative Attaché (Cultural)*
Mr. Sayed A. A. Mohamed * *Administrative Attaché (Cultural)*

EL SALVADOR

Embassy of El Salvador
8 Dorset Square 1st & 2nd Floors NW1 6PU
020 7224 9800
embajadalondres@rree.gob.sv
elsalvador.embassy@gmail.com
Monday-Friday 09.30-17.30

HER EXCELLENCY MS GILDA GUADALUPE VELÁSQUEZ-PAZ *Ambassador Extraordinary & Plenipotentiary*
(since 24 December 2019)
Mr Gerardo Heriberto Pérez-Figueroa *Minister-Counsellor*
Miss Gabriela Maria Ramirez-Lazo *Minister-Counsellor*
Ms Mayra Rosalina Barraza-Domínguez *First Secretary (Consular Affairs)*

EQUATORIAL GUINEA

Embassy of the Republic of Equatorial Guinea
13 Park Place St James' SW1A 1LP
020 7659 9090
visa@egembassy.london
www.embassyofequatorialguinea.co.uk
Monday-Friday 09.30-15.00

Vacant Ambassador *Extraordinary & Plenipotentiary*
Mrs Maria Jesús Diallo Besari * *First Secretary & Chargé d'Affaires a.i.*
Mr Pio Estéfano Mba Ndong Nvomo **m** *Second Secretary*
Mr Pedro Oscar Mba Edjang Ngoho * *Financial Attaché*

ERITREA

Embassy of the State of Eritrea
96 White Lion Street N1 9PF
020 7713 0096
Fax 020 7713 0161
www.eritrean-embassy.org.uk
pa.ambassador@eritreanembassyuk.org

HIS EXCELLENCY MR ESTIFANOS HABTEMARIAM GHEBREYESUS * *Ambassador Extraordinary &*
Plenipotentiary (since 23 September 2014)
Mr Salih Abdalla Saad * *1st Secretary*
Mr Tedros Goitom Tedla * *1st Secretary*

ESTONIA

Embassy of Estonia
44 Queen's Gate Terrace, London, SW7 5PJ
020 7589 3428
Fax 020 7589 3430
London.mfa.ee
e-mail: london@mfa.ee

HER EXCELLENCY MRS TIINA INTELMANN *Ambassador (since 4 September 2017)*
Ms Siiri Liivandi *Deputy Head of Mission*
Ms Piia Parna * *Consul*
Ms Triinu Rajasalu *Press and Public Affairs*
Mr Priit Masing **m** First Secretary (*Economic Affairs*)
Ms Kersti Kirs *Counsellor (Cultural)*
Colonel Eduard Kikas *Defence Attaché*

ESWATINI

Kingdom of Eswatini High Commission
20 Buckingham Gate SW1E 6LB
Tel: 020 7630 6611
Fax 020 7630 6564
Email: enquiries@eswatini.org.uk
Monday-Thursday 09.00-16.30 & Friday 09.00-16.00

HIS EXCELLENCY MR CHRISTIAN MUZIE NKAMBULE **m** *High Commissioner (since 7 February 2017)*
          Mrs Ncamsile Precious Nkambule
Ms Temnotfo L. C. Nkambule *Counsellor*
Ms Sithembile Prudence Lushaba *1st Secretary (Information)*
Mr Mandla Stanley Dlamini **m** *3rd Secretary*
Mrs Ruth N. Kunene **m** *Administrative Attaché*
Ms Qethuka Dlamini * *Education Attaché*

ETHIOPIA

Embassy of the Federal Democratic Republic of Ethiopia
17 Princes Gate SW7 1PZ
020 7589 7212
Fax 020 7584 7054
info@ethioembassy.org.uk
www.ethioembassy.org.uk
Monday - Friday 9.00 – 13.00 -17.00

Consular Department
020 7838 3895
Monday - Friday 9.00-13.00 & 14.00 – 16.00

Trade and Investment Department
020 7838 3870

Press Office
020 7838 3883

HIS EXCELLENCY MR FESSEHA SHAWEL GEBRE **m** Ambassador *Extraordinary & Plenipotentiary (since 26 FEBRUARY 2019)*
          Mrs Asegedech A Belayneh (Spouse)
Mr Ababi Demissie Sidelel Ambassador - Deputy head of mission
Mrs Roza Yerukneh Alemu * *Minister*
Mr Araya Gebregziabher *Minister*
Mrs Nardos Ayalew Belay **m** *Minister Counsellor I*
Mr Eshetu Yimer Aragaw **m** *Minister Counsellor I*
Mr Meknnen Amare Gebretsion **m** *Minister Counsellor I*
Mr Zerihun Abebe Yigzaw **m** *Minister Counsellor*

Mrs Workaferahu Aklilu Derseh **m** *Minister Counsellor (Business Diplomacy)*
Mr Atnafu Asfaw Amebushi * *Counsellor I (Business)*
Mr Mesfin Weldeslaassie Melkisa **m** *Counsellor II*
Mr Ermias Asmare Legesse **m** *Counsellor II*
Mr Amanual Alemu Hailu **m** *Counsellor II*
Mr Mesfin Haile Tesfay *Counsellor II (Consular)*
Ms Tsehaye Tadsse Andarga *1st Secretary (Consular)*
Mr Getachew Meseret Anley *2nd Secretary*
Mr Dimru Bekele Aschenaki *3rd Secretary (Consular Affairs)*
Mrs Banchayu Negush **m** *3rd Secretary (Ambassador's Office)*
Mrs Leul Gebregiorgis Gebregziabeher *Attache*

FIJI

High Commission of the Republic of Fiji
34 Hyde Park Gate SW7 5DN
020 7584 3661
Fax 020 7584 2838
mail@fijihighcommission.org.uk
www.fijihighcommission.org.uk
Monday-Friday 09.30-13.00 & 14.00-17.00

Consular Section
020 75843661 ext 5340/5347

HIS EXCELLENCY MR JITOKO CAKACAKABALAVU TIKOLEVU **m** *High Commissioner (Since 30 January 2016)*
        Mrs Luisa Molidrau Tikolevu
Mrs Paulini Tala Tokaduadua Cakacaka **m** *1st Secretary*
Ms Florieann Rose Cecelia Wilson *2nd Secretary*

FINLAND

Embassy of Finland
38 Chesham Place SW1X 8HW
020 7838 6200
Fax 020 7235 3680
sanomat.lon@formin.fi
www.finemb.org.uk
Monday-Friday 09.00-16.00

Finland Trade Centre
1st Floor, 239 Kensington High Street W8 6SA
020 7316 3000
perry.ledain@businessfinland.fi
Mr Harri Lanning *Vice President, Head of Region*

HIS EXCELLENCY MR MARKKU TAPIO KEINÄNEN * *Ambassador Extraordinary & Plenipotentiary (since 3 June 2019).*

Mrs Minna Joanna Laajava **m** *Minister*
Mr Jukka Matias Pajarinen **m** *Counsellor (Political Affairs)*
Mrs Päivi Elina Pihlajamäki **m** *Counsellor (Economic Affairs)*
Press Counsellor vacant
Ms Emmi Monika Kulta *Attaché (Political Affairs)*
Mrs Sari Kilpi * *2nd Secretary (Consular & Administrative Affairs)*
Colonel Pasi Viljami Saarikoski **m** *Defence Attaché*

FRANCE

Embassy of France
58 Knightsbridge SW1X 7JT

020 7073 1000
Fax 020-7073 1004
www.ambafrance-uk.org

Consular Section
21 Cromwell Road SW7 2EN
020 7073 1200
Fax 020 7073 1201

Visa Section
6A Cromwell Place SW7 2EW
020 7073 1250
Fax 020-7073 1246

Cultural Section
23 Cromwell Road SW7 2EL
020 7073 1300
Fax 020 7073 1326

Science & Technology Section
6 Cromwell Place SW7 2JN
020 7073 1380
Fax 020 7073 1390

Trade Commission – Business France
Brettenham House,
Lancaster place,
London WC2E 7EN

Taxation Section
58 Knightsbridge SW1X 7JT
020 7073 1000
Fax 020 7073 1196

Customs Section
58 Knightsbridge SW1X 7JT
Tel 020 7073 1000
Fax 020 7073 1159

Economic Section
58 Knightsbridge SW1X 7JT
Tel 020 7073 1000
Fax 020 7073 1189

HER EXCELLENCY MRS CATHERINE COLONNA *Ambassador Extraordinary & Plenipotentiary (since 2 September 2019)*

Mr François Revardeaux *Minister-Counsellor / Chargé d'Affaires*
Mr Luc Pages **m** *Defence Attaché*
Mr Jean-Christophe Donnellier *Minister-Counsellor (Economic & Financial Affairs)*
Mr Guillaume Bazard **m** *Consul General*
Mr François-Joseph Schichan *First Counsellor (Political)*
Mrs Aurélie Bonal **m** *Counsellor (Press)*
Mr Tristan Fabiani Pradeilles **m** *Counsellor (Political)*
Mr Amaud Balner *Counsellor (Political)*
Mrs Anissia Morel **m** *Legal Adviser*
Mrs Victoire Ract-Madoux **m** *Head of Cabinet, Deputy Press Counsellor*
Mrs Elisabeth Meyer *Counsellor (Political)*
Mr Nicolas Wuest-Famose *Counsellor*
Mrs Claudine Ripert-Landler **m** *Cultural Counsellor*
Mr Nicolas Le Van Xieu *General Secretary*

Mr Christian Fatras **m** *Counsellor (Economic Affairs)*
Mr Jean Arlat **m** *Counsellor (Science & Technology)*
Mr Hervé Mathevet **m** *Counsellor (Customs)*
Mrs Ariane Amson **m** *Counsellor (Judicial Affairs)*
Mr Pierre-Yves Cordier **m** *Counsellor (Nuclear)*
Mrs Nathalie Skiba **m** *Counsellor (Police)*
Mr Pierric Bonnard **m** *Counsellor (Business France)*
Mrs Marguerite Moleux **m** *Counsellor (Social Affairs)*
Mr Thomas Ernoult **m** *Counsellor (Financial Affairs)*
Mrs Heloise Pestel **m** *Counsellor (Agriculture)*
Mr Charles Denier *Deputy Consul General*
Mrs Julie Poirot **m** *Deputy Counsellor (Agriculture)*
Captain Luc Raynal **m** *Naval Attaché*
Colonel Patrice Hugret **m** *Air Attaché*
Colonel Armel Dirou **m** *Army Attaché*
Mr Nicolas Drogi *Attaché (Defence Equipment)*
Mrs Eloise Pierre **m** *1st Secretary*
Mr François Jouffroy **m** *1st Secretary*
Mr Gaetan Lehuic **m** *1st Secretary*
Mrs Chrystelle Boissière **m** *3rd Secretary (Administrative Affairs)*
Mr Benjamin Vier *Property Manager*
Mr Ahmed Driassa **m** *3rd Secretary*
Mr Yvan Ledard *3rd Secretary*
Mr Samuel Chapron *3rd Secretary*
Mrs Leila Driassa **m** *Vice Consul*
Mrs Laetitia Puchal Somme **m** *Vice Consul*
Mr Alexandre Auddin *Paymaster (Administrative Affairs)*
Mr Stéphane Jouvet **m** *Paymaster*
Mr Manuel Manzano **m** *Attaché*
Mrs Raphaelle Rodocanachi **m** *Cultural Attaché*
Mr Gérald Lalanne **m** *Attaché*
Mr Etienne Peltier **m** *Attaché (Police)*
Mr Jean-Philippe Gabilloux **m** *Cultural Attaché (Administrative Affairs)*
Mrs Stéphanie Prudent **m** *Attaché (Taxation)*
Mrs Marjorie Lecointre *Cultural Attaché (Audiovisual)*
Mr Sebastien Le Bouter *Deputy Defence Attaché (Equipment)*
Mr Francois Mercier *Attaché (Police Liaison Officer)*
Mrs Catherine Courbarien *Attaché (Protocol)*
Mr Gautier Houel *Attaché (Economic Affairs)*
Ms Marianne Carrubba *Attaché (Financial Affairs)*
Mrs Raffaella Silvetti *Attaché (Business France)*
Mrs Alice Beja **m** *Cultural Attaché for Higher Education*
Mr Stéphane Harzelec *Cultural Attaché (Administrative Affairs)*
Mrs Frederique Lefevre *Commercial Attaché (Business France)*
Mrs Krystele Petris **m** *Attaché*
Mrs Frédérique Moreira **m** *Vice Consul*
Mr Philippe Colin *Attaché (Police Liaison Officer)*
Mr Bruno Chetanneau *Attaché (Police Liaison Officer)*
Ms Lucia Da Silva *Cultural Attaché*
Ms Mathias Rambaud *Cultural Attaché (Book Department)*

GABON

Embassy of the Gabonese Republic
27 Elvaston Place SW7 5NL
020 7823 9986
Fax 020-7584 0047
gabonembassyuk@gmail.com
www.gabonembassyuk.co.uk

HER EXCELLENCY MRS AICHATOU SANNI AOUDOU *Ambassador Extraordinary & Plenipotentiary (Since 22 September 2015)*
Miss Wendy Marcelle Bilong *Counsellor (Chancery)*

Mr Lie Patrick Mouvogny **m** *Counsellor (Communications)*
Mr Hugues Lemambot Mbele *Counsellor (Protocol & Public Relations)*
Mrs Ruth Mouvogny **m** *2nd Secretary*

THE GAMBIA

The Gambia High Commission
57 Kensington Court W8 5DG
020 3928 9770
Fax 020 7229 9225
gambiahighcomuk@btconnect.com
Monday-Thursday 09.30-17.00, Friday 09.30-13.00

HIS EXCELLENCY MR FRANCIS R BLAIN *High Commissioner (since 21 November 2017)*
Mr Alieu Njie **m** *Deputy Head of Mission*
Ms Binta Charty *Finance Attaché*
Mr Abu Bakr Jawara *1st Secretary*

GEORGIA

Embassy of Georgia
20 St George's Square, SW1V 2HP
020 7348 1941
Fax 020 7603 6682
london.emb@mfa.gov.ge
www.uk.mfa.gov.ge

Consular Section
020 7348 1942
london.con@mfa.gov.ge

HER EXCELLENCY MRS TAMAR BERUCHASHVILI **m** *Ambassador Extraordinary & Plenipotentiary (Since 2 April 2016)*
          Mr Rema Gvamichava
Mrs Ekaterine Kokaia **m** *Minister & Deputy Head of Mission*
Mr George Paniashvili *Senior Counsellor*
Colonel Irakli Ninua **m** *Defence Attaché*
Ms Mary Chakvetadze *Counsellor*
Mr Giorgi Kobakhidze *Counsellor*
Mrs Mariam Tsereteli **m** *Consul*
Mrs Ana Nozadze **m** *1st Secretary*

GERMANY

Embassy of the Federal Republic of Germany
23 Belgrave Square/Chesham Place SW1X 8PZ
020 7824 1300
Fax 020 7824 1449
info@lond.diplo.de
www.uk.diplo.de

Passport & visa section by online appointment only
Fax 020 7824 1449
Visa Information Service 020 7824 1466
Passport Information Service 020 7824 1426

HIS EXCELLENCY DR PETER WITTIG **m** *Ambassador Extraordinary & Plenipotentiary (since 2 July 2018)*
          Mrs Huberta von Voss-Wittig
Mrs Julia Katharina Gross **m** *Minister (Deputy Head of Mission)*

BrigGen Ralf Raddatz **m** *Defence Attaché*
Mr Oliver Schramm **m** Minister (*Economic*)
Dr Werner Kerkloh * *Minister (Finance)*
Mr Jean Bernard Laxcroix * *Minister (Political)*
Mrs Simone Maassen-Krupke **m** *1st Counsellor (Press)*
Mr Darius Rahimi-Laridjani **m** *Minister Counsellor (Political)*
Mr Hans-Guenter Loeffler **m** *Minister Counsellor (Consular)*
Dr Ralf Teepe *1st Counsellor (Cultural)*
Mr Stephan Breidenbach **m** *Air Attaché*
Mr Matthias Schmidt **m** *Captain (Navy)*
Dr Christian Kubazcyk * *1st Counsellor (Military)*
Mr André Griese **m** *1st Counsellor (Political)*
Mr Heiner Staschen **m** *Counsellor (Social & Labour)*
Mr Rainer Sulzer **m** *Counsellor (Economic)*
Mr Frank Neumann *Counsellor (Economic)*
Mr Elmar Eich * *Counsellor (Political)*
Mr Julian Frohnecke * *Counsellor (Economic)*
Mr Wolfgang Stuetz * *Counsellor (Administration)*
Mr Heinz Decker **m** *1st Secretary (Transport)*
Mr Christian Decoster **m** *1st Secretary (Political)*
Mr Christoph Kahnert **m** *Lieutenant Colonel*
Ms Britta Schlueter *1st Secretary (Political)*
Ms Svenja Friedrich *1st Secretary (Transport)*
Mr Thomas Peter Port **m** *2nd Secretary (Police Liaison)*
Mr Jens Rohrbach **m** *2nd Secretary (Federal Police Liaison)*
Ms Olga Wittchen *2nd Secretary (Finance)*
Mrs Mariko Sara Higuchi **m** *2nd Secretary (Political)*
Mr Gerrit Moerking **m** *2nd Secretary (Political)*
Mrs Evita Isabell Diasilua **m** *2nd Secretary (Administration)*
Mrs Marlen Sulzer **m** *2nd Secretary (Administration)*
Mrs Petra Troise **m** *2nd Secretary (Administration)*
Mr Michael Hagenburger **m** *2nd Secretary (Consular)*
Mr Wolfgang Rainer Huesgen **m** *2nd Secretary (Consular)*
Mrs Petra Hanefeld **m** *2nd Secretary (Political)*
Mr Arnes Petrick * *3rd Secretary (Custom Liaison)*
Mrs Karin Schroeder **m** *3rd Secretary (Consular)*
Ms Sarah Hein *3rd Secretary (Political)*
Mr Axel Meyer **m** *3rd Secretary (Police Liaison)*
Ms Maria Rita Wolf *Attaché (Security)*
Mr Michael Marx **m** *Attaché (Security Advisor)*
Mr Michael Hirsch *Attaché (Administration)*
Mr Jan-Gerd Wilken **m** *Chief Petty Officer (Military)*
Mr Thomas Wolff *Attaché (Security)*
Ms Angela Großmann *Attaché (Consular)*
Ms Lilija Amamitch *Attaché (Consular)*
Ms Juliane Dagmar Busch **m** *Attaché (Consular)*
Ms Franziska Klein *Attaché (Press)*
Ms Sophia Elisabeth Hirthammer *Attaché (Political)*
Mr Marcus Meyer **m** *Attaché (Military)*
Mr Hendrik Martin Kim-Wolf **m** *Attaché (Administration/IT)*
Ms Susanne Haegele *Attaché (Consular)*
Mr Ulf Harring-Petersen *Attaché (Security)*
Ms Andrea Ihde **m** *Flight Sergeant*
Mrs Nora Weber **m** *Assistant Attaché (Administration)*
Mr Thomas McKinney **m** *Assistant Attaché (Military)*
Mr Egon Goebel **m** *Assistant Attaché (Administration)*
Mr Thomas Heinrich *Assistant Attaché (Security)*
Ms Afra Klinge *Assistant Attaché (Military)*
Mrs Sonja Cirrotti *Assistant Attaché (Transport)*
Mr Sascha Kaminski **m** *Assistant Attaché (Consular)*
Mrs Natalia Schaub **m** *Assistant Attaché*
Mrs Andrea Karin Le Bruen **m** *Assistant Attaché (PA Ambassador)*
Mrs Friederike Weber-Rahman **m** *Assistant Attaché (PA Deputy)*
Mr Ricco Langer *Assistant Attaché (Political)*

Ms Jacqueline Heinzelmann *Assistant Attaché (Press)*
Ms Maja von Bodungen *Assistant Attaché (Political)*
Mrs Dagmar Scholze m *Assistant Attaché (Administration)*
Mrs Cristina Murrone m *Assistant Attaché (Consular)*
Mrs Andrea Hanses *Assistant Attaché (Cultural)*
Mrs Marion Coqui m *Assistant Attaché (Economic)*
Mr Anthony Paul *Assistant Attaché (Military)*
Mr Michael Stank *Assistant Attaché (Political)*
Mr Thomas Wothe m *Assistant Attaché (Administration)*
Mr Christian Biedermann m *Assistant Attaché (Political)*
Ms Corinna Schäfer m *Assistant Attaché (Consular)*
Mrs Aysun Bruckmann-Yazici m *Assistant Attaché (Consular)*
Mr Martin Ebelt m *Assistant Attaché (Administration)*
Mr Ferdinand Wolfer *Assistant Attaché (Consular)*
Mr Benjamin Veit m *Assistant Attaché (Consular)*
Ms Julia Luethje *Assistant Attaché (Administration)*
Mr Nguyen Xuan Viet Schuermann * *Assistant Attaché (Administration)*
Mr Siegfried Schroeder m *Assistant Attaché (Administration)*
Mr Wolfgang Reschke m *Assistant Attaché (Administration)*
Mr Bernd Lehmacher m *Assistant Attaché (Administration)*

GHANA

High Commission of the Republic of Ghana
13 Belgrave Square SW1X 8PN
020 7201 5900
Fax: 020 7245 9552
Email: gh.donlon@gmail.com; ghmfa31@ghc-uk.org
Website: www.ghanahighcommissionuk.com
Monday-Friday: 09:30-13:00 and 14:00-17:00
Monday-Friday: 09:30-13:00 and 14:00-17:00 (Winter)

Passports, Immigration, Education, Trade & Investment,
IMO Affairs and Police Liaison Office
104 Highgate Hill, N6 5HE
020 8342 7501
Email: gh.donlon@gmail.com
Website: www.ghanahighcommissionuk.com
Monday-Friday: 09:30-13:00

HIS EXCELLENCY MR PAPA OWUSU-ANKOMAH m *High Commissioner (since 13 June 2017)*
            Mrs Augustina Owusu-Ankomah
Mrs Rita Tani Iddi * *Deputy Head of Mission*
Mrs Matilda Aku Alomatu Osei-Agyeman * *Minister (Head of Chancery)*
Brigadier General Isaac Mensah Tetteh m *(Defence Adviser)*
Captain (GN) Francis Ayitevi Nyarko (Deputy Defence Adviser)
Mrs Azara Al-Hassan Prempeh * *Minister (IMO Affairs)*
Ms Milana Agyeman *Minister (Treasury)*
Mr Kofi Addo m *Minister-Counsellor (Trade & Investment)*
Ms Elizabeth Apollonia Dassah * *Minister-Counsellor/Police Liaison*
Mrs Joyce Asamoah-Koranteng * *Minister-Counsellor (Commonwealth & Diaspora)*
Mr Gabriel Owusu Ansah m *Minister-Counsellor (Consular & Welfare)*
Mrs Josephine Donkor * *Minister-Counsellor (Passport & Immigration)*
Mr Charles Agyeman Attafuah * *Minister-Counsellor (Education)*
Mrs Freda Bediako-Puni * *Minister-Counsellor (Political & Economic)*
Ms Afua Gyasiwa Gaisie *Minister-Counsellor (Education)*
Mrs Adoma Dennis m *Counsellor (Consular & Welfare)*
Mr Ransford Sarpong * *Counsellor (Treasury)*
Mr Asher Safo * *Counsellor (Passport & Immigration)*
Ms Vladimira Borley Tetteh m *1st Secretary (Passport & Immigration)*
Mr Daniel Darlington Kwaku Aheto * *1st Secretary (Protocol/Administration)*
Mrs Vera Kwei * *1st Secretary (Administration)*
Mrs Celestine Kafui Quaye * *1st Secretary (Consular & Welfare)*

Ms Doris Baffour-Asare *1st Secretary (Passport & Immigration)*
Mr Godwin Yaw Tsidi **m** *1st Secretary (Finance)*
Alex Ayi Adi **m** *1st Secretary (Treasury)*
Mr Felix Adotey Pappoe **m** *2nd Secretary (Protocol)*
Mrs Patricia Afua Asamoah * *2nd Secretary (Administration)*
Ms Lydia Anorkor Lartey **m** *2nd Secretary (Finance)*
Mr Possible Banafu Hackman * *2nd Secretary (Protocol)*

GREECE

Embassy of Greece
1A Holland Park, W11 3TP.
020 7229 3850
Fax 020 7229 7221
gremb.lon@mfa.gr
www.mfa.gr/uk

Economic & Commercial Office
020 7727 8860
Fax 020 7727 9934
ecocom.london@mfa.gr

Defence Attaché's Office
020 7727 3785
Fax 020 7221 2818
London_defatt@navy.mil.gr

Consular Office
020 7313 5600-5609
Fax 020 7313 8990
grgencon.lon@mfa.gr

Police Liaison Office
020 7313 8951
Fax 020 7229 7221
grpoliceliaison@greekembassy.org.uk

National Tourism organisation Office
Great Portland House (5th Floor)
4 Great Portland Street, W1W 8QJ
020 7495 9300
Fax 020 7229 7221

Educational Affairs Office
020 7221 0093
Fax 020 7243 4212
education@greekembassy.org.uk

Maritime Affairs Office
020 7727 0507
Fax 020 7727 0509
maritime@greekembassy.org.uk

Press and Communications Office
020 7727 3071
Fax 020 7792 9054
press.lon@mfa.gr

HIS EXCELLENCY MR DIMITRIOS CARAMITSOS-TZIRAS **m** *Ambassador Extraordinary & Plenipotentiary (since 12 August 2016)*
        Mrs Margarita Mavromichalis
Mrs Pinelopi Micha *1st Counsellor (Deputy Head of Mission)*
Captain Athanasios Dimitriou **m** *Defence Attaché*

Mr Yerassimos Lazaris *Minister-Counsellor (Economic & Commercial)*
Mr Panayotis Papanastassiou **m** *1st Counsellor (Economic & Commercial)*
Mr Konstantinos Thanopoulos **m** *2nd Counsellor (Political)*
Mr Athanasios Rizos *1st Secretary (Consular)*
Mrs Eleni Soupiana **m** *Counsellor (Press & Communication)*
Mrs Georgia Velentza *1st Secretary (Economic & Commercial)*
Commodore Aristeidis Pantazoglou **m** *Maritime Attaché*
Mr Konstantinos Adamopoulos *2nd Secretary (Political)*
Ms Eleni Karali *Police Liaison Officer*
Mrs Vasiliki Tsilogianni **m** *Deputy Counsellor (Education)*
Ms Efthymia Anagnostopoulou *Adviser (Tourism)*
Mr Alkiviadis Delantonis *Counsellor (Press & Communication)*
Mrs Panagiota Syriopoulou **m** *Secretary (Press & Communication)*
Mrs Athanasia Andriopoulou **m** *Secretary (Press & Communication)*
Mrs Fersa Varouti **m** *Attaché (Consular)*
Mrs Stamatia Zygoura *Attaché (Consular)*

GRENADA

High Commission for Grenada
The Chapel, Archel Road, West Kensington W14 9QH
020 7385 4415
Fax 020 7381 4807
office@grenada-highcommission.co.uk
www.grenadahclon.co.uk
Monday-Friday 09.00-17.00
Consular Hours : Monday-Friday : 10.00-14.00

HER EXCELLENCY MS LAKISHA ABBA GRANT *High Commissioner (since 7 May 2019)*

Mr Samuel Sandy *Consul*
Ms Xiaowei Chen Diplomatic *Attaché*

GUATEMALA

Embassy of Guatemala
1st Floor & Suite1, 2nd Floor
105a Westbourne Grove W2 4UW
020 7221 1525
info@embaguate.com

Consular Section
Suite 2, 2nd Floor
105a Westbourne Grove W2 4UW
020 7221 7448
consular@embaguate.com

HIS EXCELLENCY MR ACISCLO VALLADARES MOLINA **m** *Ambassador Extraordinary & Plenipotentiary (since 05 January 2010)*
        Mrs Raquel Urruela de Valladares
Ms Olga Maria Perez Tuna *Minister-Counsellor*
Mr Pedro Gordillo *1st Secretary & Consul*
Ms Demet Maya Basaran Bethancourt *3rd Secretary*
Mrs Cecilia Santamarina de Orive **m** *Cultural Attaché*

GUINEA

Embassy of the Republic of Guinea

239 Old Marylebone Road, London, NW1 5QT
020 7258 9640/46
Fax
embassyofguinea@gmail.com

HIS EXCELLENCY MR ALEXANDRE CECE LOUA * *Ambassador Extraordinary & Plenipotentiary (since 18 November 2017)*
Mrs Ramatoulaye Sy Sangare * *Counsellor*
Mr Diguena Iromou * *1st Secretary*
Mrs Habibatou Cherif **m** *Administrative Attaché*

GUINEA-BISSAU

Embassy of the Republic of Guinea-Bissau
94 Rue St. Lazare 75009 Paris
0033 1 48 74 36 39

Vacant *Ambassador Extraordinary & Plenipotentiary*

Mrs Maria Filomena Embalo Araujo Vieira **m** *Counsellor (Economic)*
Mr José Filipe Fonseca **m** *Counsellor*
Mr Oscar Batica Ferreira **m** *1st Secretary*

GUYANA

High Commission for Guyana
3 Palace Court Bayswater Road W2 4LP
Tel: 020 7229 7684
Fax 020 7727 9809
guyanahc1@btconnect.com
www.guyanahclondon.co.uk

HIS EXCELLENCY MR FREDERICK HAMLEY CASE *High Commissioner (since 13 April 2016)*
Mrs Pegy McLennan *Counsellor*
Ms Vonetta Victor *1st Secretary*

HAITI

Embassy of the Republic of Haiti
21 Bloomsbury Way
London WC1A 2TH
0203 771 1427
Email: info.haitiuk@diplomatie.ht
Office Hours: 9:30 am to 5:00 pm

Mr Laurent Pierre Prosper * *Chargé d'Affaires & Minister-Counsellor*
Miss Fabienne Magloire *Counsellor*
Ms Anne-Gaelle Lissade **m** *1st Secretary*

HOLY SEE

Apostolic Nunciature
54 Parkside SW19 5NE
020 8944 7189
Fax 020 8947 2494
Monday-Friday 09.00-17.00

HIS EXCELLENCY ARCHBISHOP EDWARD JOSEPH ADAMS *Apostolic Nuncio (since 24 May 2017)*
Monsignor Matteo De Mori *1st Counsellor*

HONDURAS

Embassy of Honduras
4th Floor 136 Baker Street W1U 6UD
(*Building entrance is on Marylebone Road)
020 7486 4880
Fax 020 7486 4550
hondurasuk@lineone.net
hondurasembassyuk@gmail.com
www.hondurasembassyuk.co.uk
Monday-Friday 9.00-13.00 & 14.00-17.00

HIS EXCELLENCY MR IVAN ROMERO-MARTINEZ m *Ambassador Extraordinary & Plenipotentiary (since 22 January 2008)*
        Mrs. Mirian Nasser de Romero
Miss Andrea Maria Argueta-Scheib *Minister-Counsellor*
Miss Claudina Maria Martinez Argueta *1st Secretary*

HUNGARY

Embassy of Hungary
35 Eaton Place SW1X 8BY
020 7201 3440
Fax 020 7823 1348
mission.lon@mfa.gov.hu
www.mfa.gov.hu
Monday-Thursday 08.30-17.00 & Friday 08.30-14.00

Consular Department
35B Eaton Place SW1X 8BY
020 7235 5218
Fax 020 7235 8630
konz.lon@mfa.gov.hu
Monday-Friday 09.30-12.00

Economic, Investment & Trade Commission
46 Eaton Place SW1X 8AL
020 7235 8767
Fax 020 7235 4319
london@hipa.hu

Hungarian Cultural Centre
10 Maiden Lane WC2E 7NA
020 7240 8448
Fax 020 7240 4847
info@hungary.org.uk

HIS EXCELLENCY MR KRISTÓF SZALAY-BOBROVNICZKY * *Ambassador Extraordinary & Plenipotentiary (since 18 June 2016)*
Dr Beáta Margitay-Becht * *Envoy Extraordinary & Minister Plenipotentiary (Deputy Head of Mission)*
Col Viktor Makay m *Defence Attaché*
LTC Zoltán Tiszai m *Deputy Military Attaché*
Mr Lajos Oláh * *Counsellor (Head of the Consular Section)*
Mr Máté Gábor Vincze m *Director of The Hungarian Cultural Centre)*
Ms Katalin Vizi * *Counsellor (Consul)*
Ms Valéria Kicsi *1st Counsellor*
Mrs Viktória Imolyáné Kiss m *2nd Counsellor*
Mr Peter Hlinka * *1st Secretary*
Mr Csaba György Ábel * *1st Secretary*
Mr Ga'bor Takács-Carvalho m *1st Secretary (Scientific and Technology Affairs)*
Dr Anikó Zsebik * *1st Secretary (Press)*
Ms Enikő Magyar *1st Secretary*

Mr Levente Gáspár * *1st Secretary (Director General of Finance)*
Mr János Bakó **m** *2nd Secretary*
Ms Zsófia Gyombolai * *2nd Secretary*
Dr Olivér Pál Pintér **m** *2nd Secretary (Consul)*
Dr Éva Simon Second Secretary (Consul)
Mr Mihály Bóra * *3rd Secretary*
Mr Bence Spiczmüller *3rd Secretary*
Mr Ervin Simon * *3rd Secretary (Consul)*
Mr Gábor Ferenc Németh *Attaché (Finance Administrator)*

ICELAND

Embassy of Iceland
2A Hans Street SW1X 0JE
020 7259 3999
Fax 020 7245 9649
Emb.london@mfa.is
www.iceland.is/uk
Monday-Friday 09.00-16.00

HIS EXCELLENCY MR STEFAN HAUKUR JOHANNESSON **m** *Ambassador Extraordinary & Plenipotentiary (since 16 November 2017)*
        Mrs Halldora M. Hermannsdottir
Mr Ingolfur Fridriksson **m** *Counsellor*
Ms Thury Bjork Bjorgvinsdottir *1st Secretary*
Mrs Gyda Hafdis Margeirsdottir *Assistant Attaché*

INDIA

Office of the High Commissioner for India
India House Aldwych WC2B 4NA
020 7836 8484
Fax 020 7836 4331
adm.london@mea.gov.in
www.hcilondon.gov.in

HER EXCELLENCY MRS RUCHI GHANASHYAM **m** High *Commissioner (since 13 November 2018)*
        Mr Ghanashyam Ajjampur Rangaiah
Mr Charanjeet Singh **m** *Deputy High Commissioner*
Mr Vishwesh Negi **m** *Minister(Political, P&I and Extradition)*
Mr Samir Kumar Jha **m** *Minister (Consular)*
Mr Manmeet Singh Narang **m** *Minister(Coordination)*
Mr Manish Singh **m** *Minister (Economic)*
Mr Saurabh Narain **m** *Minister (Audit)*
Mr Amish Tripathi * *Director, The Nehru Centre*
Mr Anil Nautiyal **m** *Counsellor (Passport & OCI)*
Mr Amar Jit Singh * *Counsellor (Coordination & Diaspora)*
Mr Dinesh Pratap Singh **m** *Counsellor (Consular)*
Ms Smriti *Counsellor (Audit)*
Mr Bhuvana Krishnan Vellore Mohana Krishnan **m** *Military Adviser*
Air Commodore Prashant Mohan **m** *Air Adviser*
Commodore Anil Jaggi **m** *Naval Adviser*
Mrs Yamuna Sabapathy Vadivelu * *Counsellor (Technical Adviser)*
Mr Rohitkumar Rameshchandra Vadhwana **m** *1st Secretary (Economic)*
Mrs Vishakha Yaduvanshi **m** *1st Secretary (Special Assistant to High Commissioner)*
Mr Malsawmthang Keivom * *1st Secretary*
Mr Rahul Nangare **m** *1st Secretary (Trade)*
Mrs Anima Barnwal **m** *1st Secretary (ITOU)*
Mr Rohan Rajendra Samant **m** *1st Secretary (Consular)*
Mr Prem Kumar Jhell **m** *1st Secretary*
Mr Abhishek Sharma **m** *2nd Secretary (Political, Information & Education)*
Mr Manoj Sharma **m** *2nd Secretary (Head of Chancery & Protocol)*

Mr Mahesh Chawla **m** *2nd Secretary (Political & RTI)*
Mrs Chinghoihkim Keivom * 2nd Secretary
Mr Ranveer Singh Virdi **m** *2nd Secretary (Press & Information)*
Mr Abhay Kumar Toppo **m** *2nd Secretary*
Mr Sandeep Kumar **m** *2nd Secretary*
Mr Soumendra Mahapatra *m* *2nd Secretary (Visa)*
Mr Brij Kumar Guhare **m** *Deputy Director, The Nehru Centre*
Mr M.A Naqvi **m** *Third Secretary (Audit)*
Mr Sandeep Barua **m** *Third Secretary (Audit)*
Mr Nilratan Mridha **m** *Attaché (Press & Information)*
Mr Nageshwar Rao Aiysola **m** *Attaché (Commerce)*
Mr Sandeep Singh **m** *Attaché (Admn)*
Mrs Anita Kumari **m** *Attaché*
Mrs Harmohan Kaur **m** *Attaché (Coordination)*
Mr Upendra Singh Negi **m** *Attaché (Accounts)*
Mr Arijit Banerjee * *Attaché (Passport)*
Mr Ravi Shankar **m** *Attaché (Projects & Maintenance)*
Mr M S Nair Prasad **m** *Attaché*
Mrs Agnes Toppo **m** *Attaché*
Mr Rajesh Punaram Bhanarkar **m** *Attaché*
Mrs Kamal Arora **m** *Attaché*
Mr Premjeet Nireshwalia Ravindra **m** *Attaché (Visa)*
Mr Parvesh Kumar **m** *Attaché*
Mr Tarun Kumar **m** *Attaché (Hindi)*
Mr Ravi Ranjan Kumar **m** *Attaché (Audit)*
Mr Tarun Kumar **m** *Attaché (Audit)*
Mr Shiben Roy *m* *Attaché (Audit)*
Mr Sumit Kar **m** *Attaché (Audit)*
Mr Rahul Gaur *m* *Attaché (Audit)*
Mr Rajesh Roshan Azad * *Attaché (Audit)*
Mrs Anita Pokhriyal *m* *Attaché (Audit)*

INDONESIA

Embassy of the Republic of Indonesia
30 Great Peter Street SW1P 2HW
020 7499 7661
Fax 020 7491 4993
kbri@btconnect.com
www.indonesianembassy.org.uk
Monday-Friday 09.00-17.00

Consular Department & Visa Section
020 7499 7661
Fax 020 7491 4993
Consular@indonesianembassy.org.uk
Mon-Thurs 09.30-12.30, Fri-09.30-12.00 (submission of passports/visas/legalisation),
Mon-Fri 14.30-16.00 (collection of passports/visas/legalisation)

HIS EXCELLENCY DR RIZAL SUKMA **m** *Ambassador Extraordinary and Plenipotentiary (since 13 February 2016)*
    Mrs Hana Afija Satrijo
Mr Adam Mulawarman Tugio **m** *Deputy Chief of Mission*
Mrs Andalusia T. T. Dewi * *Minister Counsellor (Political Affairs)*
Mr Mohammad Iqbal **m** *2nd Secretary (Political)*
Mrs Galuh Indriana Rarasanti *3rd Secretary (Political Affairs)*
Mr Hagus Indaryanto **m** *1st Secretary (Political Affairs)*
Mr Adi Winarso **m** *Counsellor (Economic Affairs)*
Mr Bonifacius Riwi Wijayanto **m** *1st Secretary (Economic Affairs)*
Mrs I Gusti Agung Ayu Ratih Astary **m** *1st Secretary (Economic Affairs)*
Mr Thomas Ardian Siregar **m** *Minister Counsellor (Public Diplomacy, Press & Socio-Cultural Affairs)*
Mrs Juliartha Nugrahaeny Pardede **m** *1st Secretary (Public Diplomacy, Press & Socio-Cultural Affairs)*
Mrs Okky Diane Palma **m** *2nd Secretary (Public Diplomacy, Press & Socio-Cultural Affairs)*

Mr Gulfan Afero **m** *Minister Counsellor (Protocol and Consular Affairs)*
Mr Maradona Abraham Runtukahu **m** *1st Secretary (Protocol and Consular Affairs)*
Mr Muhamad Jaki Nurhasya **m** *3rd Secretary (Protocol and Consular Affairs)*
Mr Ardly Ekanata **m** *Attaché (Communication)*
Mrs Fransiska Ayu Sekar Rini ***** *Attaché (Communication)*
Mr Endang Aminudin Aziz **m** *Attaché (Education)*
Mr Lollan Andy Sutomo Panjaitan **m** *Transport Attaché*
Mr Nur Rakhman Setyoko **m** *Trade Attaché*

IRAN

Embassy of the Islamic Republic of Iran
16 Prince's Gate SW7 1PT
020 7225 4208-9
Fax: 020 7589 4440
iranemb.lon@mfa.gov.ir
www.london.mfa.ir

Consular Section
50 Kensington Court W8 5DB
020 72253000
Fax: 020 7938 1615
Iranconsulate.lon@mfa.gov.ir

HIS EXCELLENCY MR HAMID BAEIDINEJAD ***** *Ambassador Extraordinary & Plenipotentiary* (since 4 September 2016)
        Mrs Soroor Baeidinejad
Mr Seyed Mehdi Hosseini Matin **m** *Deputy Head of Mission*
Mr Reza Nuorian **m** *1st Counsellor (Political)*
Mr Saeid Zinati **m** *1st Counsellor (Consul)*
Mr Seyed Noureddin Vahed Pour *1st Counsellor (Consular Affairs)*
Mr Mesbah Ansari Dogaheh **m** *2nd Counsellor*
Mr Kiumars Javidnia **m** *2nd Counsellor*
Mr Mohammad Mirali Mohammadi ***m*** *2nd Counsellor (Press & Communications)*
Mr Morteza Kazemi Asl ***m*** *2nd Secretary (Administrative)*
Mr Naser Mohammad Zade **m** *2nd Counsellor (Consul Affairs)*
Mr Ismaeal Akrami **m** *2nd Counsellor (Consul Affairs)*
Mr Hossein Reza Entezar Yazdi **m** *1st Secretary (Political)*
Mr Hassan Davoudkhani ***m*** *1st Secretary (Financial & Administrative Affairs)*
Mr Davoud Raki **m** *3rd Counsellor (Political Affairs)*

IRAQ

Embassy of the Republic of Iraq
21 Queens Gate SW7 5JE
020 7590 7650
Fax 020 7590 7679
lonemb@mofa.gov.iq
www.mofamission.gov.iq
Monday-Thursday 09.00-16.00
Friday 09.00–15.00

Consular Section
3 Elvaston Place SW7 5QH
020 7590 9220
Fax 020 7590 9226
iraqi_consulate@hotmail.co.uk
Monday-Friday 10.00-13.00

Military Attaché Office
48 Gunnersbury Avenue W5 4HA
020 8752 1314

Fax 020 8896 0356
newiraq2ma@yahoo.com

Cultural Attaché's Office
4 Elvaston Place SW7 5QH
020 7370 2940
Fax 020 7370 2941
office@iraqiculturalattache.org.uk

Commercial Attaché Office
20 Queens Gate, London SW7 5JE
020 7584 6849
uk@iraqcomattache.com

Health Attaché Office
Embassy of the Republic of Iraq
21 Queens Gate SW7 5JE
020 7590 7650

HIS EXCELLENCY MR MOHAMMAD JAAFAR M BAKR HAIDAR AL-SADR **m** *Ambassador Extraordinary &*
Plenipotentiary (since 30 October 2019)
      Mrs Nahida Melhem
Mr Nazar Mirjan Mohammed **m** *Minister Plenipotentiary*
Ms Jwan Khioka *Minister Plenipotentiary*
Staff General Brigadier Khalaf Al Jahl **m** *Defence Attaché*
Mr Ahmad Al-Saffar **m** *Minister Plenipotentiary*
Mr Ahmed Al-Nakash **m** *Counsellor*
Mr Wael Al-Robaaie **m** *Counsellor*
Mr Mushtaq Flayeh Hassan Sultani **m** *1st Secretary*
Mr Ghassan Luaibi Mnati Saddawi **m** *1st Secretary*
Mr Hasan Hadi Talib *1st Secretary*
Mr Mostafa Al-Hassani **m** *2nd Secretary*
Mr Atheer Abood Saeed Al-Saedy **m** *2nd Secretary*
Mr Ammar Abdulhameed Farhan * *2nd Secretary*
Mr Bassam Riyadh Aziz Saleh Nema *2nd Secretary*
Mr Saifaldin Al-Darraji **m** *3rd Secretary*
Mrs Wasan Al-Husseini **m** *3rd Secretary*
Miss Sarah Alsayegh *Attaché*
Mr Mohanad Qasim **m** *Attaché*
Mr Ali Abbas Khayoon Al-Naseri *Marine Attaché*
Miss Hana Jawad Kadhem Al-Zubaidi *Commercial Attaché*
Professor Nahi Yousif Yaseen Al-Rikabi **m** *Cultural Attaché*
Mr Ali Auday Mousa Al-Khairalla **m** *Attaché*
Mr Mohammad Zuhair Al-Hiyali **m** *Attaché*
Miss Fatin Al-Hraishawi *Attaché*

IRELAND

Embassy of Ireland
17 Grosvenor Place SW1X 7HR
020 7235 2171
Fax 020 7201 2515
londonembassymail@dfa.ie
www.embassyofireland.co.uk
Monday-Friday 09.30 - 12.30 – 14.30 -16.30

Passport & Visa Office
114A Cromwell Road SW7 4ES
Passport enquiries 020 7373 4339
Visa enquiries 090 6661 0197
Diplomatic visa appointments 020 7341 5434
Fax 020 7373 4589

Passport Office Monday-Friday 09.30-16.30
Visa Office Monday-Friday 09.00-12.00 (Lodge applications), 14.30-16.00 (Collections)

HIS EXCELLENCY MR ADRIAN O'NEILL m *Ambassador Extraordinary & Plenipotentiary (since 30 August 2017*
      Mrs Aisling O'Neill
Mr Gerald Angley *Deputy Head of Mission (Political Affairs)*
Mr Cyril Francis Brennan *Counsellor (UK Foreign Policy)*
Mr Paraig Hennessy m *Counsellor (Economic & Trade Affairs)*
Ms Nicole Mannion *Counsellor (Brexit & EU Affairs)*
Mr Damien Flynn m *Counsellor (Agriculture)*
Mr David Walsh m *1st Secretary (Customs & Revenue)*
Mr John O'Sullivan m *1st Secretary (Consular & Administration)*
Mr Ruaidhri Dowling m *1st Secretary (Irish Community & Culture)*
Ms Fionnuala Callanan *1st Secretary (Press & Communications)*
Ms Rosemarie Keane *1st Secretary (Brexit & EU Affairs)*
Mr Cian O'Laoide m *1st Secretary (Finance)*
Ms Therese Walsh *1st Secretary (Economic & Trade Affairs)*
Ms Alanna Maxwell *2nd Secretary (Press & Information)*
Mr Raymond Mullen m *2nd Secretary (Political Affairs)*
Ms Sophie Jacobs *2nd Secretary (Political Affairs)*
Ms Rachel Ingersoll *2nd Secretary (Irish Community & Culture)*
Ms Rose Gaughan *Attaché (Passport Services)*
Ms Deirdre Curley *Attaché (Economic & Trade Affairs)*
Ms Ciara Kellegher m *Attaché (Visa Services)*
Mr John Freir *Attaché (Consular Services)*
Ms Celine Byrne m *Attaché (Administration)*

ISRAEL

Embassy of Israel
2 Palace Green Kensington W8 4QB
020 7957 9500
Fax 020 7957 9555
www.embassyofisrael.co.uk
Monday-Thursday 08.30-18.00 & Friday 08.45-14.00

Defence Section
2 Palace Green Kensington W8 4QB
020 7957 9530

Consular Section
15a Old Court Place Kensington W8 4QB
020 7957 9516

HIS EXCELLENCY MR MARK REGEV m *Ambassador Extraordinary & Plenipotentiary (since 4 April 2016)*
      Mrs Vered Regev
Mrs Sharon Bar Li m *Minister-Deputy Head of Mission*
Mrs Ilana Ravid m *Consul*
Mrs Vivian Aisen m *Minister-Counsellor (Public Affairs)*
Mr Eyal Azoulay m *Minister-Counsellor*
Mr Elad Ratson m *Counsellor (Public Affairs)*
Mr Yehuda Avivi m *Counsellor (Press)*
Ms Dana Erlich m *Counsellor*
Mr Yariv Becher m *Minister (Commercial Affairs)*
Colonel Tidhar Dar m *Defence Attaché*
Mrs Sharon Ehrlich Bershadsky m *1st Secretary (Tourist Affairs)*
Mr Ofer Grinboim-Liron m *1st Secretary*
Mr Sivian Holder m *1st Secretary*
Mr Michael Freemen m *1st Secretary*

ITALY

Embassy of Italy
14 Three Kings' Yard, Davies Street, W1K 4EH
020 7312 2200
Fax 020 7312 2230
ambasciata.londra@esteri.it
www.amblondra.esteri.it

Consular Section
Harp House, 83-86 Farringdon Street, EC4A 4BL
020 7936 5900
Fax 020 7583 9425
consolato.londra@esteri.it
www.conslondra.esteri.it

Cultural Section
39 Belgrave Square, SW1X 8NX
020 7235 1461
Fax 020 7235 4618
icilondon@esteri.it
www.icilondon.esteri.it

Defence Section (Military, Naval & Air Attaché's Offices)
7-10 Hobart Place, SW1W 0HH
020 7259 4500
Fax 020 7259 4511
londra.coad4@smd.difesa.it

Financial Section
2 Royal Exchange, EC3V 3DG
020 7606 4201
Fax: 020 7929 0434
london.office@bancaditalia.co.uk

Trade Commission
Sackville House
40 Piccadilly, W1J 0DR
020 7292 3910
Fax: 020 7292 3911
londra@ice.it
www.ice.gov.it
HIS EXCELLENCY MR RAFFAELE TROMBETTA **m** *Ambassador Extraordinary & Plenipotentiary (since 29 January 2018)*
      Mrs Victoria Jane Mabbs
Mr Alessandro Motta ***** *Minister & Deputy Head of Mission*
General Enrico Pederzolli **m** *Defence Attaché*
Mr Marco Villani ***** *1st Counsellor (Consul General)*
Mr Fabrizio Colaceci **m** *1st Counsellor (Political Affairs)*
Mr Massimo Carnelos **m** *1st Counsellor (Economic Affairs)*
Mr Gianluca Brusco **m** *1st Counsellor (Political Affairs)*
Mr Alberto La Bella **m** *Counsellor (Cultural Affairs & Press Office)*
Mr Francesco De Angelis **m** *1st Secretary (Consul)*
Mr Salvatore Marinò **m** *1st Secretary*
Mr Diego Solinas **m** *1st Secretary (Consul)*
Ms Francesca Maria Dell'Apa *1st Secretary*
Lt. Co. Augusto Vizzini **m** *Deputy Defence Attaché*
Colonel Claudio Petrozziello **m** *Attaché (Customs, Excise & Tax Affairs)*
Ms Luisa Tondelli ***** *Attaché (Scientific Affairs)*
Mr Luca Golzi *Attaché (Police Affairs)*
Prof. Anna Chimenti ***** *Attaché*
(vacant position) *Attaché (Cultural Affairs - Director)*
Mr Ferdinando Pastore **m** *Attaché (Trade Commissioner)*
Mr Maurizio Ghirga **m** *Attaché (Financial Affairs)*
Mr Luigi Raimondo Maligno *Attaché (Administrative Affairs)*

Ms Filomena Maria Gatto * *Attaché (Administrative Affairs)*
Mr Guglielmo Caggiano m *Attaché (Economic Affairs)*
Mr Domenico Maria De Giorgio m *Attaché (Administrative Affairs)*
Mrs Carmela Buonomo m *Attaché (Administrative Affairs)*
Ms Clementina Osti *Attaché (Administrative Affairs)*
Mrs Marisa Vivani m *Attaché (Consular Affairs)*
Mr Lorenzo Arcari m *Attaché (Consular Affairs)*
Ms Antonietta Ruggiero *Attaché (Consular Affairs)*
Mrs Giuseppina Bove m *Attaché (Consular Affairs)*
Ms Daniela Avitabile * *Attaché (Consular Affairs)*
Mrs Solange Medici m *Attaché (Consular Affairs)*
Mr Domenico Pellegrino m Attaché *(Consular Affairs)*
Mr Stefano Faggioli *Attaché (Cultural Affairs)*
Mr Nicola Locatelli *Attaché (Cultural Affairs)*

JAMAICA

Jamaican High Commission
1-2 Prince Consort Road
London
SW7 2BZ
020 7823 9911
Fax 020 7589 5154
jamhigh@jhcuk.com
www.jhcuk.com
Monday-Thursday 09.00-17.00 & Friday 09.00-16.00

Passport & Visa Section
Monday-Friday 9.30-13.30

HIS EXCELLENCY SETH GEORGE RAMOCAN, CD m *High Commissioner (since 22 December 2016)*
          Dr. Lola Ramocan
Mrs. Angella Rose-Howell m *Deputy High Commissioner*
Mrs. Tracey Ann Blackwood m *Minister-Counsellor (Diaspora & Consular Affairs)*
Miss Carol Lee-Lea *Counsellor (Diaspora & Consular Affairs)*
Mrs. Renee Lloyd m *Counsellor, (Political & Economic Affairs)*
Mr. Cedric Brentnol Salmon * *1st Secretary (Finance & Administration)*
Miss Deyneka Beckford *Attaché (Finance & Administration)*
Mrs. Juliet Dennison m *Attaché (Administration)*
Mr. Laurence Jones m *Attaché (Commercial)*
Mrs. Marcia Evadney Chung-Ying * *Attaché*
Mrs. Claudette Barrett Francis m *Attaché (Administration)*

JAPAN

Embassy of Japan
101-104 Piccadilly W1J 7JT
020 7465 6500
Fax 020 7491 9348
Monday-Friday 09.30-18.00
Visa Section 020 7465 6565 Fax 020 7491 9328
Information Section 020 7465 6500 Fax 020 7491 9347
www.uk.emb-japan.go.jp

HIS EXCELLENCY MR YASUMASA NAGAMINE m *Ambassador Extraordinary & Plenipotentiary (since 7 June 2016)*
          Mrs Ayako Nagamine
Mr Takashi Okada m *Envoy Extraordinary & Minister Plenipotentiary*
Mr Minoru Nakamura m *Minister (Finance)*
Mr Takeshi Ito m *Minister (Information)*
Mr Jun Miura m *Minister (Political)*
Mr Satoshi Katahira m *Minister (Economics)*

MsTakako Tsujisaka *Minister and Consul General*
Mr Yoshifumi Yoshikawa **m** *Counsellor (Economic)*
Mr Takashi Ishitobi **m** *Counsellor (Political)*
Mr Isao Shimizu **m** *Counsellor (Transport)*
Mr Akira Shimizu **m** *Counsellor (Accounts)*
Mr Kazutaka Fujii * *Counsellor (Telecommunications)*
Mr Shuichi Matsumoto **m** *Counsellor (Economic)*
Mr Kazushi Izuchi **m** *Counsellor (Administration)*
Mr Osamu Ashizuka **m** *Counsellor (Political)*
Mr Susumu Tsuda **m** *Counsellor (Consular)*
Captain Naoki Abe **m** *Defence Attaché*
Mr Koichiro Sakamoto **m** *1st Secretary (Administration)*
Mr Toshinori Sano * *1st Secretary (Information)*
Mr Tetsuya Kishimoto **m** *1st Secretary (Economic)*
Mr Norikazu Tamura * *1st Secretary (Telecommunications)* .
Mr Koichi Ozaki **m** *1st Secretary (Political)*
Mr Toshiyuki Hatano * *1st Secretary (Political)*
Mr Naoya Maeda **m** *1st Secretary (Political)*
Mr Yugo Wakabayashi **m** *1st Secretary (Political)*
Ms Akiko Fujimoto **m** *1st Secretary (Information)*
Mr Koji Tanaka **m** *1st Secretary (Consular)*
Mr Yusuke Ishihara **m** *1st Secretary (Economic)*
Mr Koji Ogawa **m** *1st Secretary (Economic)*
Mr Yoshitaka Nakano **m** *1st Secretary (Political)*
Mr Kazuya Nakao **m** *1st Secretary (Transport)*
Mr Hayato Sunaga **m** *1st Secretary (Information)*
Mr Atsushi Goto **m** *1st Secretary (Economic)*
Ms Katsue Chikama *1st Secretary (Consular)*
Mr Shuhei Kataoka **m** *1st Secretary (Finance)*
Mr Masaru Suzuki *1st Secretary (Economic)*
Mr Takuya Tanimoto * *1st Secretary (Political)*
Mr Manabu Ishizuka **m** *1st Secretary (Economic)*
Mr Masahiro Katayama *2nd Secretary (Political)*
Mr Takahiro Omori **m** *2nd Secretary (Political)*
Ms Yumiko Honda **m** *1st Secretary (Economic)*
Mr Harui Saito * *2nd Secretary (Security)*
Ms Maki Machiyama **m** *2nd Secretary (Culture and Information)*
Mr Ryo Oshida **m** *2nd Secretary (Accounts)*
Ms Kaoru Saiki *2nd Secretary (Information)*
Mr Kazunori Otsuka **m** *2st Secretary (Finance)*
Mr Toru Yoshikawa **m** *2nd Secretary (Consular)*
Mr Kazumasa Miyashita **m** *2nd Secretary (Consular)*
Ms Hikari Nishimoto **m** *2nd Secretary (Protocol)*
Ms Aki Yano *2nd Secretary (Information)*
Mr Megumi Nakahara **m** *2nd Secretary (Security)*
Mr Yutaro Mochida *2nd Secretary (Political)*
Mr Hideaki Matsumae *2nd Secretary (Economic)*
Mr Masahiro Tanaka 2nd *Secretary (Telecommunications)*
Miss Arisa Chisaki *Attaché (Information)*
Ms Ami Taniguchi *Attaché (Account)*
Mr Yuta Nagai **m** *Attaché (Administration)*

JORDAN

Embassy of the Hashemite Kingdom of Jordan
6 Upper Phillimore Gardens W8 7HA
020 7937 3685
Fax 020 7937 8795
london@fm.gov.jo
www.jordanembassy.org.uk
Monday-Friday 09.00-16.00

Consular & Visa Section
6 Upper Phillimore Gardens W8 7HA

Monday-Friday 10.00-13.00 & 14.30-16.00

Defence Attaché's Office
16 Upper Phillimore Gardens W8 7HA
020 7937 9611
Fax 020 7937 7505
Monday-Thursday 09.00-15.00, Friday 09.00-12.00

HIS EXCELLENCY MR OMAR B. AI- NAHAR **m** *Ambassador Extraordinary & Plenipotentiary (since 27 October 2017)*
        Mrs Hiba Muheissen Al-Nahar
Miss Raya Nayef Saoud Kadi *Minister Plenipotentiary*
Alsharifeh Noor Ali Hassan Abu Assam *1st Secretary*
Princess Haya Bint Al Hussein *1st Secretary*
Miss Razan Mohammad Abdulhameed Alsaket *2nd Secretary*
Brig. Gen. Amin Ali Salman Qatarmeh * *Military Attaché*
Col. Abdel Hameed Macknay *Assistant Military Attaché*
Lt. Col. Samer Kamel Dawood Graeb * *Military Liaison Officer*
Lt. Col. Ahmed Fadel Mohammad Hammouri * *Procurement Officer and Liaison Officer for Alhussein Project*
Lt. Col. Mohammad Yusef Ahmad Al-Makahleh * *Military Finance Officer*
Maj. Baha Aldeen Izzat Ahmad Alkurdi **m** *Training & Education Officer*
Captain Ahmed Mahmoud Mohammed Al-Zoubi * *Medical Officer*

KAZAKHSTAN

Embassy of the Republic of Kazakhstan
125 Pall Mall, London SW1Y 5EA
Tel: 020 792 51757
Fax 020 7930 8990
Email: London@kazembassy.org.uk; London@mfa.kz
www.mfa.kz/london
Monday-Friday 09.00-13.00 & 14.30-18.30

Consular Section
Tel: 020 7925 7532 *(only on working days between 12:00 & 13:00)*
Emergency Tel: +44(0)7447470570
Fax: 020 7389 0600
Email: consulate@kazembassy.org.uk;
Monday-Friday 09.30-12.30 *(except Wednesday)*

HIS EXCELLENCY MR ERLAN IDRISSOV **m** *Ambassador Extraordinary & Plenipotentiary (since 27 February 2017)*
        Mrs Nurilla Idrissova
Mr Zhabolat Ussenov **m** *Minister-Counsellor (Political Affairs)*
Mr Anuar Kurzhikayev **m** *Counsellor (Economic Affairs)*
Colonel Ruslan Khomutov **m** *Defence, Military, Naval and Air Attaché*
Mr Bauyrzhan Zharmagambetov **m** *Counsellor*
Mr Alibek Razakov **m** *Counsellor*
Mr Azamat Kairolda **m** *Counsellor*
Mr Dauren Doszhanov **m** *Counsellor*
Mr Rustam Tazhenov **m** *1st Secretary (Economic Affairs)*
Mr Maxat Ibrayev **m** *Counsellor*
Ms Ainur Nazarymbetova *1st Secretary (Consul)*
Mr Meriam Duyssimbinov **m** *1st Secretary*
Mr Zharas Ormantay **m** *2nd Secretary*
Mr Darkhan Faizulin **m** *Assistant Military Attaché*
Mr Darkhan Abzhanov **m** *3rd Secretary*
Mrs Aigerim Seisembayeva **m** *3rd Secretary (Press Secretary)*
Mr Anuar Adilbekov **m** *3rd Secretary*
Mr Yerzhan Joshibayev **m** *Attaché (Vice Consul)*
Mr Artur Lastayev *Special Representative of the Prosecutor General of Kazakhstan in European countries (Resident in Geneva)*

Ms Zhuldyz Missalimova *Attaché (Head of Chancery)*

KENYA

Kenya High Commission
45 Portland Place
London W1B 1AS
Tel: 0207 636 2371
Fax: 0207 323 1932
www.kenyahighcom.org.uk

HIS EXCELLENCY MR CALEB MANOA ESIPISU **m** *High Commissioner (since 28 December 2018)*
      Mrs Waithiegeni Kanguru-Esipisu
Mr Allan Mburu **m** Minister-Counsellor I
Mr James Kiiru **m** *1st Counsellor*
Mr Peter Njiru **m** *2nd Counsellor*
Mr Aden Mohamed **m** *1st Secretary*
Mr Isaac Wangunyu **m** *1st Secretary*
Col. Joseph Mokwena **m** *Defence Adviser*
Mrs Anne Kamau **m** *Commercial Counsellor*
Mr Evans Kinyanjui **m** *Immigration Attaché*
Mrs Dorothy Kamwilu **m** *Education Attaché*
Ms Rebecca Toto **m** *Immigration Attaché*
Mr Ayub Munyifwa **m** *Financial Attaché*

KIRIBATI

London Honorary Consulate (see Honorary Consuls section below)

KOREA (DEMOCRATIC PEOPLE'S REPUBLIC OF)

Embassy of the Democratic People's Republic of Korea
73 Gunnersbury Avenue W5 4LP
Tel 020 8992 4965
Monday-Friday 09.00-12.00 & 14.00-17.00
prkinfo@yahoo.com

HIS EXCELLENCY MR IL CHOE **m** *Ambassador Extraordinary & Plenipotentiary (since 10 November 2016)*
      Mrs Yong Ae Kim
Mr Song Gi Kim **m** *Minister*
Mr Kwang Min Kim **m** *Counsellor (Deputy Permanent Representative to IMO)*
Mr Tong IL Ryang **m** *2nd Secretary*
Mr Ju Hyon Hwang **m** *3rd Secretary*

KOREA (REPUBLIC OF)

Embassy of the Republic of Korea
60 Buckingham Gate SW1E 6AJ
020 7227 5500/2
Fax 020 7227 5503
Website http://gbr.mofa.go.kr
Monday-Friday 09.00-12.00 and 13:30-17.30

Press & information Office
020 7227 5500 (ext. 615)

Consular Section
020 7227 5500 - 7
Monday – Friday 9.00-12.00 and 14:00-16.00

Visa Section
Monday-Friday 10.00-12.00

Korean Cultural Centre
Grand Buildings 1-3 Strand WC2N 5BW
020 7004 2600
Fax 020 7004 2619
www.kccuk.org.uk
Monday-Friday 10.00-18.00 & Saturday 11.00-17.00

HER EXCELLENCY MS ENNA PARK m *Ambassador Extraordinary & Plenipotentiary (since 20 August 2018)*
　　Mr Won-Soo Kim
Mr Nahmkook Sun m *Minister (Deputy Head of Mission)*
Mr Jang Won Hong m *Minister*
Mr Hongsik Kim * *Minister-Counsellor (Financial)*
Mr Sang Keun Song * *Minister-Counsellor*
Mr Jung Woo Lee * *Minister-Counsellor (Cultural)*
Mr Sojin Hwang m *Counsellor (Political)*
Mr Kyoungmin Ko m *Counsellor*
Mr Gyeong Hun Yim m *Counsellor*
Mr Taek Lim Oh m *Counsellor (Interior)*
Mr Sunghoon Hwang m *1st Secretary (Science & ICT)*
Mr Sung Ho Min m *1st Secretary (Press & Information)*
Mr Hee Hoon Kang m *1st Secretary (Procurement)*
Mr Hyun Soo Park m *1st Secretary (Police)*
Mr Seyong Park m *1st Secretary (Legislative)*
Mr Kee Joon Nam m *1st Secretary*
Mr Sang Min Moon m *1st Secretary*
Mrs Eun Jung Lee m *1st Secretary (Political)*
Mr Jeongho Park m *1st Secretary*
Mrs In Jung Park m *2nd Secretary (Head of Administration)*
Ms Suyeon Kim *2nd Secretary*
Ms Jisung Yoo m *2nd Secretary*
Mr Jangwon Lee m *3rd Secretary*
Mr Jong Ha Kim * *3rd Secretary*
Captain Jihoon Kim m *Defence Attaché*
Lt. Col.Dongjin Jeong m *Air Attaché*
Ms Soo Kyeong Kim m *Attaché (Education)*

KOSOVO (REPUBLIC OF)

Embassy of the Republic of Kosovo
8 John Street WC1N 2ES
Tel: 020 7405 1010
embassy.uk@rks-gov.net
Monday–Friday 09.00–17.00

Consular Section
Tel: 020 7025 0995
consulate.london@rks-gov.net

Vacant *Ambassador Extraordinary & Plenipotentiary*
Ms Heroina Telaku m *Minister Counsellor*
Miss Arrita Gjakova *Minister Counsellor*
Mr Berat Havolli *Minister Counsellor*
Mr Imer Berisha * *Minister Counsellor*
Miss Elmaze Pireva *Counsellor (Economic and Commercial Affairs)*
Lt Col Beton Retkoceri m *Defence Attaché*
Mrs Vjollca Halimi m *1st Secretary (Consular Section)*
Miss Liridona Hertica *2nd Secretary (Consular Section)*

KUWAIT

Embassy of the State of Kuwait
2 Albert Gate SW1X 7JU
020 7590 3400/3406/3407
Fax 020 7823 1712
Monday-Friday 09.00-16.00

Cultural Office
Hyde Park House 60A Knightsbridge SW1X 7JX
020 7761 8500
Fax 020 7761 8505
https://kcouk.org/ksims/welcome.htm

Kuwait Military Office
Hyde Park House 60A Knightsbridge SW1X 7LF
020 7761 2800/2811
Fax 020 7761 2810/2820

Kuwait Health Office
40 Devonshire Street W1G 7AX
020 7307 1700
Fax 020 7323 2042

Kuwait Investment Office
Wren House 15 Carter Lane EC4V 5EY
020 7606 8080
Fax 020 7332 0755

HIS EXCELLENCY MR KHALED AL-DUWAISAN GCVO **m** *Ambassador Extraordinary & Plenipotentiary (since 29 April 1993)*
Mrs Dalal Al-Duwaisan
Mr Nawaf Bushaibah **m** *Counsellor (Deputy Head Mission)*
Mr Khaled AlKhulifah *1st Secretary*
Mr Zaid AlHarb **m** *1st Secretary*
Mr Abdullah AlWenayyan **m** *2nd Secretary*
Mr Abdulaziz AlThuwaikh *Attaché (Political)*
Mr Fahad AlMudhaf **m** *Attaché*
Mr Ahmad Alfailakawi **m** *Attaché*
Mr Jabir Alkandari **m** *Attaché*
Mr Ghazi Almershed *Attaché*
Mr Ahmad AlSaeedi *Attaché*
Mr Rakan AlDhafiri *Attaché*
Mr Khaled AlAli **m** *Attaché*
Mr Muthana S S Aladsani **m** *Attaché*
Brig. Gen. Saif Mohammad *Military Attaché*
Col Yousef Marafi **m** *Military Attaché (Assistant Military Attaché)*
Lt Col Abdullah Alsabah *Military Attaché (Assistant Military Attaché for Administration)*
Lt Col Dr Abdullah Alkhadher *Military Attaché (Assistant Military Attaché for Technical Affairs)*
Major Alsabeeh Sabeeh *Assistant Military Attaché for Financial Affairs*
Dr Fawzia Al-Sayegh **m** *Military Attaché (Health)*
Dr Fawzan AlFares **m** *Attaché (Head of Cultural Office)*
Dr Fahad AlMudhaf **m** *Attaché*
Mrs. Sarah Alawadhi **m** *Attaché*
Dr Abdulaziz Ahmad AlRasheed * *Health Attaché (Health Attaché for Medical Affairs)*
Mr Nayef Alrashidi **m** *Health Attaché (Assistant Health Attaché for Administration)*
Mr Saleh Alateeqi **m** *Financial Attaché (Head of the Kuwait Investment Office)*
Mr Mohammed Al Kharafi *Financial Attaché*
Mr Abdulah Al-Shamlan *Financial Attaché*
Mr Fahad AlSahli *Financial Attaché*
Mr Ali Ibraheem AlQadhi *Financial Attaché*
Mr Mohammad Alderbass *Financial Attaché*

Mr Mohammed AlMenaifi *Financial Attaché*
Mr Ahmad Al-Ateeqi *Financial Attaché*
Mr Abdullah AlHadlaq *Financial Attaché*
Mr Abdulatif Adel M.A.H. Alroumi *Financial Attaché*
Mr Hasan Behbehani *Financial Attaché*
Mr Khalifah Hamad Kh H Alasousi **m** *Financial Attaché*
Miss Tala Zalzalah *Financial Attaché*
Mr Meshari Almutairi *Financial Attaché*
Mr Abdulaziz AlJasem **m** *Financial Attaché*
Mr Abdulaziz AlMajed *Financial Attaché (Legal Advisor)*
Mr Saud AlAmiri **m** *Financial Attaché (Auditor)*

KYRGYZSTAN

Embassy of the Kyrgyz Republic
Ascot House 119 Crawford Street W1U 6BJ
020 3865 1994
mail@kyrgyz-embassy.org.uk
www.kyrgyz-embassy.org.uk
Monday-Friday 09.00-18.00

Consular Section
020 3865 1994 (ext. 1907)
kyrgyzconsuluk@gmail.com
Monday-Friday 10.00-13.00

HIS EXCELLENCY MR EDIL BAISALOV *Ambassador Extraordinary & Plenipotentiary (since 06 August 2019)*
Ms Lira Sabyrova *Counsellor*
Mr Elnur Tagaev **m** *1st Secretary & Consul*

LAOS

Embassy of the Lao People's Democratic Republic
49 Porchester Terrace W2 3TS
020 7402 3770
Fax 020 7262 1994
laosemblondon@gmail.com

HIS EXCELLENCY MR PHONGSAVANH SISOULATH **m** *Ambassador Extraordinary & Plenipotentiary* (since 13
February 2019)
        Mrs Monekeo Sisoulath
Mr Keo Vongxay *Minister-Counsellor*
Ms Nuanvilay Rattanakone *2nd Secretary*
Mr Sengphaivone Nanthaphone *3rd Secretary*
Ms Niphonekham Khammounheuang *3rd Secretary*

LATVIA

Embassy of the Republic of Latvia
45 Nottingham Place W1U 5LY
020 756 31 619
Fax 020 7312 0042
embassy.uk@mfa.gov.lv
http://www.mfa.gov.lv/en/london/

Consular Section
The Grove House
248a Marylebone Road
NW1 6JF
020 7725 9212
Fax 020 7312 0042

consulate.uk@mfa.gov.lv

HER EXCELLENCY MRS BAIBA BRAŽE m *Ambassador Extraordinary & Plenipotentiary (since 24 August 2016)*
  Mr Tjaco Van Den Hout
Mrs Katarina Platere m *Deputy Head of Mission*
Mrs Mara Fricberga *Counsellor & Head of Consular Section*
Mr Kaspars Lejietis m *Counsellor (Ministry of Justice)*
Mr Aigars Mikisko m *Counsellor (Defence)*
Mr Valts Vitums m *Counsellor (Consular Affairs)*
Mr Oskars Fridmanis m *1st Secretary (Finance and Administration)*
Mr Kaspars Krumholcs *2nd Secretary (EU Affairs & Diaspora Affairs)*
Mrs Ilze Vituma m *2nd Secretary (Visa Officer, Consular Affairs)*
Mr Ansis Hercogs m *3rd Secretary (Consular Affairs)*
Mr Edgars Strautmanis m *Police Liaison Officer*
Mr Reinis Azis *Economic Attaché, Head of the Representative Office of Latvian Investment & Development Agency*

LEBANON

Embassy of Lebanon
21 Kensington Palace Gardens W8 4QN
020 7727 6696/7792 7856
Fax 020 7243 1699
emb.leb@btinternet.com

Consular Section
15 Palace Gardens Mews W8 4RB
020 7229 7265

HIS EXCELLENCY MR RAMI MORTADA m*Ambassador Extraordinary & Plenipotentiary (since 9 November 2017)*
  Mrs Jamal Yehia
Mr Marwan Francis m *Counsellor (Deputy Head of Mission)*
Miss Rasha Haddad *1st* Secretary
Miss OulaKhodr *1st* Secretary
Brig. Gen NazihAkiki m *Military Attaché*
Mr Ralph Nehme m *EconomicAttaché*

LESOTHO

High Commission of the Kingdom of Lesotho
7 Chesham Place Belgravia SW1X 8HN
020 7235 5686
Fax 020 7235 5023
hicom@lesotholondon.org.uk
lesotholondon@gmail.com
www.lesotholondon.org.uk
Monday-Friday 09.00-16.00

HER EXCELLENCY MRS RETHABILE MAHLOMPHO MOKAEANE m *High Commissioner (since 11 April 2019)*
  Mr Pitso Clement Mokaeane
Ms Lineo Alphoncinah Palime *Counsellor*
Mr Nkopane Thabane *1st Secretary*
Mrs Mantolo Motloheloa m *3rd Secretary*

LIBERIA

Embassy of the Republic of Liberia
23 Fitzroy Square W1T 6EW
020 7388 5489
Fax 020 7388 2899
info@embassyofliberia.org.uk

www.embassyofliberia.org.uk
Monday-Friday 10:30-17:00 Spring-Autumn (Chancery closed at 16:30 during winter months)

HER EXCELLENCY MRS GURLY T. GIBSON **m** *Ambassador Extraordinary & Plenipotentiary (since 6 February 2019)*
       Mr Harald Dieter Schwarz
Ms Marian F. Sandi **m** *Minister-Counsellor & Chargé d'Affaires*
Mr Albert Kjlatoe Jaja **m** *Minister-Counsellor*
Ms Winifred Y Nelson-Gaye **m** *Attaché*
Mr Harry Conway **m** *Policy Officer and Maritime Attaché*

LIBYA

Embassy of Libya
15 Knightsbridge SW1X 7LY
020 7201 8280
Fax 020 7245 0588
Telex 266767
Monday-Friday 09.30-15.30

Consular Section
61-62 Ennismore Gardens SW7 1NH
020 7589 6120
Fax 020 7589 6087

Academic Unit
61-62 Ennismore Gardens SW7 1NH
020 7581 2393

Press Office
15 Knightsbridge SW1X 7LY
020 7201 8280
Fax 020 7245 0588

Vacant *Ambassador Extraordinary & Plenipotentiary*

Mr Mohamed Elkoni * *Charge d'Affaires a.i.*
Mr Ahmed Rmalli * *Minister Plenipotentiary*
Mr Hasan Toumi * *Counsellor*
Mr Farhat Farjallah **m** *Counsellor*
Mr Esam Matous **m** *Counsellor (Administration)*
Mrs Maha Othman **m** *Consular Affairs Counsellor*
Miss Ebtisam Alsiti *1st Secretary*
Mr Badreddin Giloshi **m** *1st Secretary*
Mrs Nadra Elbeshti **m** *1st Secretary*
Mr Faiz Elagielli **m** *1st Secretary*
Mrs Enas Kaal **m** *1st Secretary*
Mr Hussain Khill **m** *Consular Officer*
Mr Ali Elkarom *Defence Attaché*
Mr Aimin Omran **m** Academic Attaché
Mr Basher Drirah *Cultural Attaché*
Mr Elhassan Elfadil **m** *Assistant Cultural Attaché*

LITHUANIA

Embassy of the Republic of Lithuania
Lithuania House 2 Bessborough Gardens SW1V 2JE
020 7592 2840
Fax 020 7592 2864
amb.uk@urm.lt
http://uk.mfa.lt

Commercial Attaché's Office

020 7592 2862
Fax 020 7592 2864

Consular Section
Monday 13.00-17.00, Tuesday-Friday 9.00-13.00

Visa Section
Tuesday, Wednesday & Thursday 15.00-16.00

HIS EXCELLENCY MR RENATAS NORKUS **m** *Ambassador Extraordinary & Plenipotentiary (since 18 August 2017)*
      Mrs Sandra Smaidryte
Mr Jonas Grinevičius **m** *Minister Plenipotentiary*
Mrs Natalija Bacevičiené **m** *Minister Counsellor (Diaspora)*
Ms Renata Radvilaite *Counsellor (Consular Affairs)*
Ms Asta Chaladauskiené *Counsellor (Political Affairs)*
Mrs Erika Griesiuviene **m** *Counsellor (Consular Affairs)*
Mrs Jovita Radziunaite-Kaleininkiene **m** *3rd Secretary*
Ms Aurelija Laurušonyté **m** *3rd Secretary*
Colonel Vidmantas Raklevičius **m** *Defence Attaché*
Mr Linas Pernavas * *Police Attaché*
Mr Zamzickas Mantas **m** *Commercial Attaché*
Ms Juste Kostikovaite *Cultural Attaché*
Mrs Ingrida Sotlandaite-Juzefoviciene **m** *Chief Officer (Finance & Administration)*

LUXEMBOURG

Embassy of Luxembourg
27 Wilton Crescent SW1X 8SD
020 7235 6961
Fax 020 7235 9734
londres.amb@mae.etat.lu
Monday-Friday 09.00-17.00

Consular Section
Visa Office Monday-Friday 10.00-11.45

HIS EXCELLENCY MR JEAN ALFRED OLINGER **m** *Ambassador Extraordinary & Plenipotentiary (since 16 August 2017)*
      Mrs Véronique Olinger-Masquelin
Mr Jean-Marie Frentz **m** *Deputy Head of Mission*
Ms Sylvie Gilberte Muschang *1st Secretary (Chancellor)*
Mr Christophe Tommy Zeeb-Ichter *Counsellor (Legal & Financial Affairs)*

MADAGASCAR

Embassy of the Republic of Madagascar
5th Floor, One Knightsbridge Green SW1X 7NE
020 7052 8277
ambamad.contact@madagascarembassy.org.uk

Vacant *Ambassador Extraordinary & Plenipotentiary*

Mrs Anjaniaina Olivia Rakotonirina **m** *Counsellor and Chargé d'Affaires a.i.*
Mr Tojonirina Ramarolahy *1st Counsellor*
Mr Maminarivo Andrianatoandro **m** *Administrative & Consular Attaché*

MALAWI

High Commission of the Republic of Malawi
36 John Street WC1N 2AT

020 7421 6010
Fax 020 7831 9273
malawihighcommission@btconnect.com
www.malawihighcommission.co.uk
Monday-Friday 09.30-13.00 & 14.00-17.00

HIS EXCELLENCY MR KENNA ALEWA MPHONDA **m** *High Commissioner (since 18 June 2015)*
        Mrs Mary Chokani Mphonda
Mrs Quent Madalo Kalichero **m** *Deputy High Commissioner*
Brigadier General Sydney Crispen Linyama **m** *Defence Attaché*
Mr Peter Chilinda **m** *1st Secretary (Finance)*
Mrs Towera Zimba Mmodzi **m** *1st Secretary (Admin & Diaspora)*
Mrs Martha Sanyala Gonondo **m** *1st Secretary (Consular)*
Mr Kondwani Munthali *2nd Secretary (Press & Protocol)*
Mr Mwayi Dausi *3rd Secretary (Consular)*

MALAYSIA

Malaysian High Commission
45-46 Belgrave Square SW1X 8QT
020 7235 8033
Fax 020 7235 5161
mwlon@btconnect.com
Monday-Friday 09.00-17.00
Visa/Consular Monday-Friday 09.00-12.00

Adminstration
020 7919 0254

Protocol
020 7919 0253

Consular
020 7919 0210

Immigration
020 7919 0230

Defence
020 7919 0274

Economic
020 7499 4644 (Trade)
020 7919 0616 (Investment)

Education/Students
020 7985 1252

Tourism
020 7930 7932

Maritime
020 7919 0249

HIS EXCELLENCY DATUK MOHAMAD SADIK KETHERGANY **m** *High Commissioner (since 27 April 2019)*
        Mrs Datin Jakkiah HJ Basran
Mr Mohd Suhaimi Jaafar **m** *Deputy High Commissioner*
Prof Dr Shafie Mohamed Zabri **m** *Counsellor (Education)*
Mr Rohizal Mohd Radzi * *Counsellor (Education)*
Mr Khairil Azwan Abu Mansor **m** *Counsellor (Education)*
Mr Mohammad Shaarul Md Osman *Counsellor (Police Liaison)*
Mrs Rashida Othman * *Counsellor (Investment)*
Mr Allen Mohd Salleh **m** *1st Secretary (Police Liaison)*

Mr Megat Iskandar Ahmad Dassilah **m** *Counsellor (Commercial)*
Mr Mohd Sayuti Shaari **m** *Attaché (Immigration)*
Mr Mohd rozaimi Harun **m** *Minister*
Mr Samzah Jamirin **m** *2nd Secretary (Political)*
Ms Qairunnisa MD Alias *Counsellor (Political)*
Mrs Hilyati Salwa Shokri **m** *1st Secretary (Political)*
Brig. Gen. Subari Tomo **m** *Defence Adviser*
Maj. Hairulnizam Baharuddin **m** *Assistant Defence Adviser*
Mr Shah ZulmizanSafar **m** *Education Attaché*
Mr Hanizam Darham **m** *Education Attaché*
Miss Nik Eylia Sofia AbdAziz *Education Attaché*
Mr Firdaus Zakaria **m** *Education Attaché*
Mr Ruzain Syukur Mansor **m** *Attaché (Education)*
Mr Kanagalingam T Selvarasah **m** *Attaché (Maritime)*
Mr Shaari Rais **m** *2nd Secretary (Education)*
Mr Jesse Quiban **m** *1st Secretary (Bilateral)*
Ms Nur Haniza Jaafar *1st Secretary (Police Liaison)*
Ms. NoritaMohdNoor *3rd Secretary (Administration)*
Mrs Sofiah Othman **m** *2rd Secretary*

MALDIVES

High Commission of the Republic of Maldives
22 Nottingham Place W1U 5NJ
020 7224 2135
Fax 020 7224 2157
info@maldivesembassy.uk
www.maldivesembassy.uk
Monday-Friday 09.30-16.30

HER EXCELLENCY DR FARAHANAZ FAIZAL **m** *High Commissioner (since 1 February 2020, Ambassador
Extraordinary & Plenipotentiary between 18 May 2019 and 31 January 2020)*
        Dr Mohamed Ahmed Didi
Mr Mohamed Nazeer **m** *Minister (Trade Representative)*
Mr Mamdhooh Ismail **m** *1st Secretary*
Ms Shahiya Ali Manik **m** *1st Secretary*
Ms Fareena Aishath *2nd Secretary*
Mrs Asima Hassan **m** *3rd Secretary*

MALI

Embassy of the Republic of Mali
Avenue Molière 487 1050 Brussels BELGIUM
00 322 345 74-32
Fax 00 322 344 57 00

Vacant *Ambassador Extraordinary & Plenipotentiary*

Mr Mamounou Toure **m** *Counsellor*

MALTA

Malta High Commission
Malta House 36-38 Piccadilly W1J OLE
020 7292 4800
Fax 020 7734 1831
maltahighcommission.london@gov.mt
www.foreign.gov.mt
Monday-Friday 09.00-13.00 & 14.00-17.00

High Commissioner's Private Secretary
020 7292 4827

Political
020 7292 4826

Commonwealth
020 7292 4825

EU/Trade Section
020 7292 4826

Consular/Information/Citizenship Section
020 7292 4806
Citizenship.london@gov.mt

Visa Section
020 7292 4821
Visa.london@gov.mt

Passport Section
020 7292 4807
Passports.london@gov.mt

Medical Section
020 7292 4829
Medical.london@gov.mt

Pensions Section
020 7292 4821

HIS EXCELLENCY MR JOSEPH COLE **m** *High Commissioner (since 1 August 2018)*
        Mrs Bernardina Cole
Ms Chantal Sciberras *Deputy High Commissioner*
Ms Deborah Maria Borg *Counsellor (Political)*
Ms Christine Said *Consul 1st Secretary*
Dr Michaela Muscat *Maritime Attaché*
Mr Peter Paul Meli *Economic Attaché*

MAURITANIA

Embassy of the Islamic Republic of Mauritania
Carlyle House, 235-237 Vauxhall Bridge Road SW1V 1EJ
020 7233 6158

HIS EXCELLENCY DR ISSELKOU AHMED IZID BIH NEYE **m** *Ambassador Extraordinary & Plenipotentiary (Since 16 October 2018)*
        Mrs Mariem Sidi Bouna
Mr El Alem Hamza **m** *1st Counsellor*
Mr Mohamed Mohamedou **m** *1st Counsellor*
Mr Mohamed Bouya Mohamed Elghith **m** *2nd Counsellor*

MAURITIUS

Mauritius High Commission
32/33 Elvaston Place SW7 5NW
020 7581 0294
Fax 020 7823 8437 / 020 7584 9859
londonhc@govmu.org
londonconsul@govmu.org (consular matters only)
Monday-Friday 09.30-13.00 & 14.00-17.00

HIS EXCELLENCY MR GIRISH NUNKOO m *High Commissioner (since 09 August 2015)*
    Mrs Bibi Qamarara Nunkoo
Mr Khemraj Jingree m *Minister Counsellor/Deputy High Commissioner*
Mr Thailesh Kumar Chamane m *1st Secretary*
Mr Dooshant Kumar Bucktowar m *2nd Secretary*
Mr Uttamsingh Goodur m *2nd Secretary*
Miss Nirmala Rewa *Counsellor (Economic Matters)*

MEXICO

Embassy of Mexico
16 St. George Street W1S 1FD
Switchboard: (44-20) 7499 8586
E-Mail: mexuk@sre.gob.mx
Web Page: http://www.sre.gob.mx/reinounido
Monday-Friday 09.00-13.00 & 14.00-15.00

Consular Section
16 St. George Street W1S 1FD
consulmexuk@sre.gob.mx

Military & Air Section
8 Halkin Street SW1X 7DW
Tel & Fax: (44-20) 7235 7898

Naval Affairs Section
8 Halkin Street SW1X 7DW
Tel & Fax : (44-20) 7235 6211

Maritime Affairs Section
8 Halkin Street SW1X 7DW
Tel : (44-20) 7235 8475

Commercial Section
8 Halkin Street SW1X 7DW
Tel: (44-20) 7811 5041

Tourism Section
Wakefield House
41 Trinity Square EC3N 4DJ
Tel: (44-20) 7488 9392

Vacant *Ambassador Extraordinary & Plenipotentiary*
Mrs Aureny Aguirre O.Sunza m * *Ambassador/Minister (Alternate Representative to the IMO & Multilateral Affairs Attaché)*
Mr Adrian Esteban Santos Ruiz * *Counsellor (Press Affairs)*
Mrs Aida Guillermina Velasco Perez * *Head of the Consular Mission*
Ms Mónica Valdez Murphree m *2nd Secretary (Political Affairs Attaché)*
Mr Melendrez Armada Rodrigo m *2nd Secretary (Scientific and Cooperation Affairs Attaché)*
Mr Juan Carlos Lombardo Muñoz Ledo *3rd Secretary (Economic Affairs Attaché)*
Ms Stephanie Marie Black León *3rd Secretary (Cultural Attaché)*
Rear Admiral Leopoldo Jesús Díaz González Solórzano m *(Permanent Alternate Representative to the IMO)*
Rear Admiral Fernando Rodríguez Cuevas m *Naval Attaché*
Mr Oscar Toledo Martinez m *Deputy Naval Attaché*
Captain Pedro Gabriel Pineda Berdeja m *Assistant Naval Attaché*
Colonel Marco Antonio Dominguez Sanchez m *Military and Air Attaché*
Mr Olvera Dominguez Tonatiuh m *Deputy Military & Air Attaché*
Mr Alberto José Martinez Salinas *1st Secretary, Alternate Representative to the IMO*
Mr Vicente Salas Hasselbach m *Counsellor (Tourism Attaché)*

MOLDOVA

Embassy of the Republic of Moldova
5 Dolphin Square Edensor Road W4 2ST
020 8995 6818
020 8995 6927
embassy.london@mfa.gov.md
www.regatulunit.mfa.gov.md
Monday-Friday 08.00-13.00 & 14.00-17.00

Consular & Visa section
020 8996 0546
consul.london@mfa.gov.md
Monday-Friday 08.00-13.00 & 14.00-17.00

HER EXCELLENCY MRS ANGELA PONOMARIOV m *Ambassador Extraordinary & Plenipotentiary (since 28 September 2018)*
       Mr Stefan Martin Christian Kesseleökeöi Majthényi Báró
Mrs Oxana Borta m *Counsellor*
Ms Cristina Jandic *2nd Secretary (Consular Affairs)*

MONACO

Embassy of the Principality of Monaco
7 Upper Grosvenor Street London W1K 2LX
0207 318 1081
Fax 0207 493 4563
www. embassy-to-uk.gouv.mc/en
embassy.uk@gouv.mc

HER EXCELLENCY MRS EVELYNE GENTA *Ambassador Extraordinary & Plenipotentiary (since 12 January 2010)*

MONGOLIA

Embassy of Mongolia
7-8 Kensington Court
London W8 5DL
Tel: 020 7937 0150
Fax: 020 7937 1117
E-mail: chancery@embassyofmongolia.co.uk
Website: www.embassyofmongolia.co.uk

HIS EXCELLENCY MR TULGA NARKHUU *Ambassador Extraordinary & Plenipotentiary (since 11 September 2018)*
       Mrs Burmaa Batbold
Mr Ganbold Gankhuyag, *Minister-Counsellor (Political Affairs)*
Mr Munkhdemberel Lundeejantsan *Counsellor (Trade and Economic Affairs)*
Ms Enkhtuya Ganzorig *2nd Secretary (Political and Cultural Affairs)*
Ms Oyunjargal Ulziitogtokh *2nd Secretary (IMO, Consular Affairs)*
Mr Munkhtushig Bayarbat *Attaché (Consular Affairs)*

MONTENEGRO

Embassy of Montenegro
47 De Vere Gardens W8 5AW
020 3302 7227
Fax 020 3302 7227
unitedkingdom@mfa.gov.me

HIS EXCELLENCY MR BORISLAV BANOVIĆ m *Ambassador Extraordinary & Plenipotentiary (since 02 February 2016)*
       Mrs Vesna Banović
Mr Mladen Dragasevic m *Minister Counsellor*
Captain (N) Darko Vukovic m *Defence Attaché*

Mrs Valentina Kneżevic-Tomic m *1st Secretary*

MOROCCO

Embassy of the Kingdom of Morocco
49 Queens Gate Gardens SW7 5NE
0207 581 5001-4,
Fax 0207 225 38 62
ambalondres@maec.gov.ma
www.morocanembassylondon.org.uk
Monday-Friday 09.00-17.00

Consular Section
Diamond House: 97/99 Praed Street, Paddington, W2 1NT
Tel: 0207 724 07 19/0207 724 06 24
Fax: 0207 7067407
Consmorocco.uk@lycos.co.uk

HIS EXCELLENCY MR ABDESSELAM ABOUDRAR m *Ambassador Extraordinary & Plenipotentiary (since 10 November 2016)*
   Mrs Saloua Larhrissi
Miss Lalla Soumia Bouhamidi *Deputy Head of Mission*
Col. Tarik Refae m *Military & Naval & Air Attaché*
Lt Colonel Mostafa Tafrhy m *Deputy Defence Attaché & Representative to the IMO*
Mr Brahim Outti m *Counsellor*
Ms Najla Benmbarek *Counsellor*
Mr Khalid El Moujaddidi m. *Consul General*
Mr Mostafa Zaitouni m *Counsellor- Deputy Consul*
Mrs Fatima Azzahra Manouri m Counsellor- *Vice Consul*
Mr Najib Essadki *1st Secretary (Political)*
Miss Hanane Maoulainine *1st Secretary (IMO)*
Mrs Machichi Siham *1st Secretary (Cultural Affairs)*
Mr Marouan Abousif *1st Secretary (Economic Affairs)*
Mr Salima El Fadili *1st Secretary (Economy)*
Miss Myriam Sekkouri Alaoui *1st Secretary (Press)*
Mr Ahmed Biyoud m *Vice Consul*
Mrs Laila Kairouani m *Vice Consul*
Mr Abdelkrim Missi m *Vice Consul*
Ms Sanae Ougaddoum *Attaché*
Mr Tissir Es-Sadraty m *Attaché*
Mr Abdelmajid Chabab *Attaché*
Mr Jamal El Achaoui m *Security Attaché*
Mr Rachid Amrani m *Security Attaché*
Mr Taoufiq Benhajjou m *Security Attaché*

MOZAMBIQUE

High Commission for the Republic of Mozambique
21 Fitzroy Square W1T 6EL
020 7383 3800
sectorconsular@mozambiquehc.co.uk
www.mozambiquehighcommission.org.uk
Monday-Friday 09.30-13.00 & 14.00-17.00
Consular Section: Monday-Friday 09.30-13.00; Inquiries by telephone: Monday-Friday 14.30-16.30

HIS EXCELLENCY MR FILIPE CHIDUMO m *High Commissioner (Since November 2015)*
   Mrs Paula Marisa Frederico Chidumo
Mr Omar Remane m *Minister-Counsellor*
Mr Aurélio Machimbene Matavele Júnior m *1st Secretary*
Ms Rabeca Albino Raimundo *Consular Attaché*
Mrs Teresa Jose Samuel Baila Vieira * *Financial & Administrative Attaché*

MYANMAR

Embassy of the Republic of the Union of Myanmar
19A Charles Street W1J 5DX
General Office 020 7148 0740
Ambassador's Office 020 7148 0749
Political, Trade, Press & Cultural Affairs Section 020 7148 0741
Consular Section 020 7148 0740
Fax 020 7409 7043
ambassadoroffice@londonmyanmarembassy.com
consular@londonmyanmarembassy.com
www.londonmyanmarembassy.com

HIS EXCELLENCY KYAW ZWAR MINN **m** *Ambassador Extraordinary & Plenipotentiary (since 28 October 2013)*
          Mrs Aye Minn Myat
Dr Chit Win **m** *Minister-Counsellor*
Captain (Navy) Soe Aung * *Defence Attaché*
Mr Chit Khaing * 1st Secretary
Ms Su Myat Thu *1st Secretary*
Mr Kyaw Myint * *2nd Secretary*
Ms Thiri Thandar Lwin 2nd Secretary
Mr Min Khaing Kyar Nyo **m** *3rd Secretary*
Mr Ye Lin Aung **m** *3rd Secretary*
Ms Yamin Yu **m** *Chief of Chancery/Attaché*
Ms Nu Nu Wai *Attaché*
Mr Han Myo Lwin **m** Attaché
Mr Aung Naing Saw **m** *Attaché*
Mr Aung Thet Htwe **m** *Attaché*
Mr Min Min Htike **m** *Attaché*

NAMIBIA

High Commission for the Republic of Namibia
6 Chandos Street W1G 9LU
020 7636 6244
Fax 020 7637 5694
info@namibiahc.org.uk
Monday to Friday 09.00-13.00 & 14.00-17.00

HER EXCELLENCY MS LINDA ANNE SCOTT *High Commissioner (since 19 December 2018)*
Mr George Tshatumbu **m** *Minister-Counsellor (IMO)*
Mr O'Brien Simasiku *1st Secretary (Commonwealth, Education & Culture & Politics)*
Mrs Ruth Kangwiya **m** *2nd Secretary (Finance & Administration)*
Ms Amabel Leticia Strauss * *3rd Secretary*

NAURU

London Honorary Consulate (see Honorary Consuls section below)

NEPAL

Embassy of Nepal
12A Kensington Palace Gardens W8 4QU
020 7229 1594/6231/7243 7853
Fax 020 7792 9861
eon@nepembassy.org.uk
www.uk.nepalembassy.gov.np
Monday-Friday 09.00-13.00 & 14.00-17.00

HIS EXCELLENCY DR DURGA BAHADUR SUBEDI m *Ambassador Extraordinary & Plenipotentiary & Permanent Representative to the IMO, ICO, ITC & WEC (since 29 September 2016)*
    Mrs Poonam R Subedi
Mr Sharad Raj Aran m *Counsellor & Deputy Chief of Mission*
Brig. Gen. Kumar Babu Thapa Chhetry m *Military Attaché*
Mr Lawa Subedi m *2nd Secretary*
Mr Tejendra Regmi m *3rd Secretary*

NETHERLANDS

Embassy of the Kingdom of the Netherlands
38 Hyde Park Gate SW7 5DP
020 7590 3200
LON@minbuza.nl
https://www.netherlandsworldwide.nl/countries/united-kingdom
Monday-Friday 09.00-17.00

Ambassador's Office
020 7590 3299
Fax 020 7590 3262

Political Department
020 7590 3294
Fax 020 7590 3262

Economic Department
020 7590 3259

Press, Public Diplomacy & Cultural Department
020 7590 3269

Operational Management Department
020 7590 3252

Consular Department
020 7590 3200
Fax 020 7581 3458

Defence Attaché's Office
020 7590 3244

Army Attaché's Office
020 7590 3244

Agricultural, Nature & Food Quality Department
020 7590 3279

Netherlands Foreign Investment Agency
020 7590 3286

HIS EXCELLENCY MR SIMON SMITS m *Ambassador Extraordinary & Plenipotentiary (since 11 September 2015)*
    Mrs Astrid Kleinen
Mrs Brechje Schwachöfer m *Minister Plenipotentiary*
Ms Anne Marie Stordiau-van Egmond *Counsellor (Security and Justice)*
Mr Arjan Dieder Uilenreef m *Counsellor (Political Affairs)*
Mrs Jacoba Louise Maria Van der Loo m *1st Secretary (Political Affairs)*
Mr Deniz Horzum m *2nd Secretary (Political Affairs)*
Ms Patricia Zandstra *1st Secretary (Economic Affairs)*
Mr Khoa Bui *2nd Secretary (Economic Affairs)*
Mr Roland Van de Ven *1st Secretary (Press & Cultural Affairs)*
Mr Mattheus Maria Klomp m *2nd Secretary (Operational Management)*
Captain Wolter Sillevis Smitt m *Defence and Naval Attaché*
Lt Colonel Rob Arts m *Military, Air and Deputy Defence Attaché*

Mr Patrich Voss **m** *Strategic Liaison Officer (Police)*
Mr Edwin Coppens * *Liaison Officer (Police)*
Mr Tim Heddema **m** *Agriculture Attaché*
Mr Ties Rinze Henk Elzinga **m** *Counsellor (Netherlands Foreign Investment Agency)*
Ms Veerle Yasmijn van Ginkel *1st Secretary (Netherlands Foreign Investment Agency)*

NEW ZEALAND

New Zealand High Commission
2nd Floor New Zealand House 80 Haymarket SW1Y 4TQ
Monday-Friday 09.00-17.00

Chancery
020 7930 8422
Fax 020 7839 4580
www.mfat.govt.nz/uk
Enquiries: enquiries@newzealandhc.org.uk
Consular: consular@newzealandhc.org.uk

Defence Staff & Defence Purchasing Office
020 7930 8400
Fax 020 7930 8401

Immigration New Zealand
020 3582 7499 (Visa Application Centre)
Fax 020 7973 0370

Passport Office
020 7968 2730
Fax 020 7968 2739

New Zealand Trade & Enterprise
020 7321 5371
Fax 020 7973 0104

HIS EXCELLENCY THE RT HON SIR JERRY MATEPARAE **m** *High Commissioner (since 27 March 2017)*
      Lady Janine Mateparae
Mr David Evans *Deputy High Commissioner*
Brigadier Christopher Parsons **m** *Defence Adviser & Head New Zealand Defence Staff*
Mr Nicholas Swallow **m** *Counsellor (Commercial)*
Mr Christopher Page **m** *Counsellor (Police)*
Mr Chris Kebbell **m** *Counsellor (Primary Industries)*
Mr Andrew Badrick *Counsellor (Customs)*
Mrs Jane Tapley **m** *Counsellor (Management) and Consul General*
Mr Carl Mann *Counsellor*
Ms Katharyn Osborn *Counsellor*
Mr David Koziarski *1st Secretary (Political)*
Ms Emily Sanders *1st Secretary (Immigration)*
Mr Deighton Conder **m** *1st Secretary (Trade & Economics)*
Ms Laura Young *1st Secretary (Economic & Bilateral)*
Ms Rosalie Miller *2nd Secretary (Multilateral)*
Mr Aaron Gallen *Attaché*
Commander Tony Masters **m** *Naval Adviser*
Lieutenant Colonel Emma Thomas **m** *Military Adviser*
Lieutenant Commander Zia Jones **m** *Logistics Adviser*
Warrant Officer Stephen Clarke **m** *Business Manager*

NICARAGUA

Embassy of Nicaragua
Suite 2 Vicarage House 58-60 Kensington Church Street W8 4DB
020 7938 2373
Fax 020 7937 0952

embaniclondon@btconnect.com
www.cancilleria.gob.ni

Consular Section
consulnic.uk@btconnect.com

HER EXCELLENCY GUISELL MORALES-ECHAVERRY *Ambassador Extraordinary & Plenipotentiary (since 15 January 2015)*
Mr Ricardo Carioni Morales **m** *1st Secretary & Deputy Head of Mission*

NIGER

Embassy of the Republic of Niger
154 Rue de Longchamp 75116 Paris FRANCE
(00) 331 45 04 80 60
Fax (00) 331 45 04 79 73

HIS EXCELLENCY ADO ELHADJI ABOU *Ambassador Extraordinary & Plenipotentiary (Since 5 February 2018)*
Mr Aminou Elh Malam Manzo *1st Counsellor*
Mr Amadou Hassane Mai Dawa *2nd Counsellor*
Mr Ichaou Amadou *1st Secretary*
Mr Aboubacar Alzouma Yandou *1st Secretary*

NIGERIA

High Commission for the Federal Republic of Nigeria
Nigeria House 9 Northumberland Avenue WC2N 5BX
020 7839 1244
Fax 020 7839 8746
Monday-Friday 09.30-17.30
chancery@nigeriahc.org
information@nigeriahc.org.uk
www.nigeriahc.org.uk

Immigration Section
9 Northumberland Avenue WC2N 5BX
020 7839 1244
Fax 020 7925 0990
passport@nigeriahc.org.uk
visa@nigeriahc.org.uk
Monday-Friday 10.00-13.00

Defence Section
9 Northumberland Avenue WC2N 5BX
020 7839 1244
Fax 020 7925 1483

HIS EXCELLENCY GEORGE ADESOLA OGUNTADE **m** *High Commissioner* (since 09 October 2017)
        Mrs. Modupe Oguntade
*Deputy High Commissioner (*Vacant)
Mrs Martha Okpi-Nnoli **m** *Minister/Chief of Protocol*
Mr Ahmed Sule **m** *Minister/Head (Industry, Trade & Investments)*
Mr Mohammed Shehu Kangiwa **m** *Minister (Head of Immigration)*
Mr Olukayode Aluko **m** *Minister/Head of Information Culture & Sports*
Mr Emmanuel A. Namah **m** *Minister/Head (Consular, Education and Welfare)*
Mr Wilson Leva Malgwi **m** *Third Secretary (Consular, Education and Welfare)*
Mr Basil M. Okolo **m** *Minister/Deputy Head of C E & W*
Mr Paulinus Uchenna Nwokoro **m** *Minister/Political*
Mr Oludare Ezekiel Folowosele **m** *Minister/Deputy (Head of immigration)*
Mr Enock N. Gazi **m** *Minister/Deputy Head (Information, Culture & Sports)*

Mrs Imaobong Effiong-Archibong **m** *Counsellor (Political)*
Mrs Rose Yakowa-Okoh *Counsellor (Industry, Trade & Investments)*
Mr Dantoye Igbanibo George **m** *Counsellor (Information, Culture & Sports*
Mr Isoken Ikponmwosa **m** *Counsellor (Industry, Trade & Investments)*
Mrs Suliat A Paramole **m** *1st Secretary (C E & W)*
Mrs Helen U. Nzeako **m** *1st Secretary (Head of Chancery)*
Mr Henry G. Odunna **m** *1st Secretary (Political)*
Mrs Esther Ahumibe **m** *2nd Secretary (Admin)*
Mrs Linda A. Pama **m** *3rd Secretary (Administration)*
Mr Alfred A. Bamidele **m** *Finance Attaché*
Mr Dada S. Eguaroje **m** *Admin Attaché (OCB)*
Mrs Kehinde O. Ogunbiyi **m** *Admin Attaché (C E & W)*
Mrs Helen E. Taddy **m** *Admin Attaché (High Commissioner's Office)*
Mrs Ngozi J. Nzekwe **m** *Admin Attaché (Protocol)*
Mr Auwalu Garba **m** *Admin Attaché (Administration)*
Mr Yusuf Sule **m** *Admin Attaché (Administration)*
Mr Reginald F. Orji **m** *Admin Attaché (D-bags)*
Mrs Mary A. Ushie **m** *Immigration Attaché*
Mr Mohammed Kaila **m** *Deputy Immigration Attaché II*
Mr Aliyu Suleiman **m** *Deputy Immigration Attaché III*
Mr Taiwo A. Hundeyin **m** *Deputy Immigration Attaché IV*
Brigadier Gen. Abubakar Sadiq Ndalolo **m** *Defence Adviser*
Maj. Eniola Bankole Oguntuase **m** *Deputy Defence Adviser (Finance)*
Wg. Cdr. Fauziyyu Sani Maaji *Deputy Defence Adviser (Air)*
Commander Mutalib Ibikunle Raji **m** *Deputy Defence Adviser (Navy)*
Major Charles C. Odugu **m** *Deputy Defence Adviser (Lib)*
MWO Abdullahi Jantulu **m** *CC/PA- Defence Adviser*
Mr Dikko Tahir Bala **m** *Alternate Permanent Representative to the IMO*
Engr. Anas Kawu Suleiman **m** *Deputy Alternate Permanent Representative to the IMO*
Mr Bwala William Auta **m** *Chief Maritime Officer to the Alternate Rep to IMO*
Mr Y M Kankiya **m** *Liaison Officer to National University Commission (NUC)*

NORTH MACEDONIA

Embassy of the Republic of North Macedonia
Suites 2.1 & 2.2 Second Floor Buckingham Court,
75-83 Buckingham Gate, London SW1E 6PE
020 7976 0535
sek.london@mfa.gov.mk
www.mfa.gov.mk (Ministry of Foreign Affairs)

HER EXCELLENCY MS ALEKSANDRA MIOVSKA *Ambassador Extraordinary & Plenipotentiary (since 5 September 2018)*

Mrs Eli Bojadjieska Ristovski **m** *Minister-Counsellor (Political & Economic)*
Mrs Katerina Mihajlova **m** *2nd Secretary (Consular)*

NORWAY

Royal Norwegian Embassy
25 Belgrave Square SW1X 8QD
020 7591 5500
Fax 020 7245 6993
emb.london@mfa.no
www.norway.org.uk

HIS EXCELLENCY MR. WEGGER CHRISTIAN STRØMMEN **m** *Ambassador Extraordinary & Plenipotentiary (as of the 2nd of January 2019)*
        Reverend Doctor Cecilie Jørgensen Strømmen
Ms Vibeke Rysst-Jensen *Deputy Head of Mission*
Ms Ragnhild Øverjordet **m** *Counsellor (Head of Administrative & Consular Section)*
Mrs Kristin Maroy Stockman **m** *Counsellor (Cultural Affairs & Trade Policy)*

Mrs Mari Olsen m *Counsellor (Security & Defence Policy)*
Ms Inger Elisabeth Meyer * *Counsellor (Political)*
Mr Simen Svenheim m *Counsellor (Trade, Industry & Fisheries)*
Ms Kaja Glomm m *Counsellor (Political)*
Mr Stein-Ivar Lothe Eide m *1st Secretary (Political)*
Mr Are Berentsen *Consul (Consular)*
Mr Sigrud Andreas Moe m *Police Attaché*
Colonel Dr.Professor John Andreas Olsen m *Defence Attaché*

OMAN

Embassy of the Sultanate of Oman
167 Queens Gate, London SW7 5HE
Switchboard: 020 7225 0001
Fax: 020 7589 2505
london2@mofa.gov.om
london1@mofa.gov.om

Information Attaché
020 758 0202
Fax: 020 7589 7751
info_attache@btconnect.com

Military Attaché
33 Thurloe Square
London SW7 2SD
Fax: 020 7584 3653

Cultural Attaché
Winchester House
259-269 Old Marylebone Road
London NW1 2RA
020 7838 3853
020 7838 3826
m.alamri@omanembassy.org.uk

Health Attaché
167 Queens Gate
London SW7 5HE
020 7225 0001
Fax: 020 7589 2505
london1@mofa.gov.om

HIS EXCELLENCY ABDULAZIZ ABDULLAH ZAHIR AL HINAI m *Ambassador Extraordinary & Plenipotentiary (since 12 November 2009)*
          Mrs Maryam *Talib Ali Al Hinai*
Shaikh Ghassan Ibrahim Shaker m *Minister Plenipotentiary*
Dr Omar Abdul Munim Al-Zawawi m *Counsellor*
Mr Issa Saleh Abdullah Saleh Al Shibani m *Deputy Head of Mission*
Mr Al Sayyid Hamyar Hilal Hamed Al Sammar Al Busaid m *Minister Plenpotentiary*
Miss Rua Issa Ashraf Al Zadjali *Counsellor*
Mr Issa Saleh Al Rashdi m *Counsellor*
Mr Mohammed Abdullah Salim Al Zeidi *1st Secretary*
Miss Amal Ali Hassan Al Balushi *1st Secretary*
Mr Zayed Mussallam Jamaan Qatamim Al Mahroon m *1st Secretary*
Sheikh Saud Mustahail Ahmed Al Mashani m *2nd Secretary*
HH Theyazin Haitham Tarik Al Said *2nd Secretary*
Mr Abdullah Abbas Al Kindi *2nd Secretary*
Commodore Said Ali Khalfan Al Maqbali m *Military Attaché*
Wing Commander Ali Sid Al Habsi m *Assistant Military Attaché*
Major Malik Abdullah Al Mamari m *Military Attaché*
Mr Musallam Taman Al-Amri m *Cultural Attaché*
Mr Mohammed Khalfan Khamis Al Busaidi m *Information Attaché*

PAKISTAN

High Commission for the Islamic Republic of Pakistan
35-36 Lowndes Square SW1X 9JN
020 7664 9276
Fax 020 7664 9224
phclondon@phclondon.org
www.phclondon.org
Monday-Friday 09.30-17.30

Consular Division
34 Lowndes Square SW1X 9JN
Monday-Thursday 10.00-12.30 & Friday 10.00-12.00

HIS EXCELLENCY MR MOHAMMAD NAFEES ZAKARIA **m** *High Commissioner (since 21 January 2019)*
    Mrs Nelofar Qureshi
Mr Muhammad Ayub **m** *Deputy High Commissioner*
Mr Muazam Ali **m** *First Secretary (Political)*
Mr Muhammad Aneel Zafar **m** *First Secretary (Political)*
Mr Faisal Mahmood **m** *First Secretary*
Mr Dildar Ali Abro **m** *First Secretary (Consular Affairs)*
Mr. Muhammad Jawad Ajmal **m** *Second Secretary*
Commodore Jamal Alam **m** *Defence & Naval Adviser*
Captain Abid Rafique **m** *Defence Procurement Adviser*
Colonel Rana Muhammad Asif **m** *Army & Air Adviser*
Mr Muhammed Waqas **m** *Counsellor (PATLO)*
Major Umer Shaukat Ali **m** *1st Secretary PATLO-II*
Mr Ghulam Nabi Memon **m** *Minister (Coord)*
Mr Sher Abbas **m** *Counsellor (Coord)*
Mr Muhammad Baqar Raza **m** *First Secretary*
Mr Nazar Hussain **m** *First Secretary (Technical Attaché)*
Muneer Ahmad **m** *(Press Attaché)*
Mr Sajid Mehmood **m** *Commercial Counsellor*
Mr Muhammad Luqman Masood **m** *Director (Audit & Accounts)*
Mr Rehmat Ullah **m** *ACMA/ Second Secretary*
Mr Taj Wali **m** *Assistant Director (MRP)*
Mr Hasan Ali Zaigham **m** *Counsellor*
Mr Ghulam Qadir **m** *Manager (NADRA)*
Mr Shafiq Ahmad Shahzad **m** *Counsellor (Trade & Investment)*

PALAU

London Honorary Consulate (see Honorary Consuls section below)

PANAMA

Embassy of Panama
40 Hertford Street W1J 7SH
020 7493 4646
Fax 020 7493 4333
panama1@btconnect.com

Consulate General
40 Hertford Street W1J 7SH
020 7409 2255
Fax 020 7493 4499
legalizations@panamaconsul.co.uk

HER EXCELLENCY MRS IRMA NATALIA ROYO RUIZ DE HAGERMAN **m** *Ambassador Extraordinary & Plenipotentiary (since 6 November 2019)*
    Mr Santiago Hagerman Arnus

Miss Karla Patricia Gonzalez Rodriguez *Minister-Counsellor, Deputy Head of Mission*
Miss Ana Cecilia Alvarado *Counsellor*
Mr Musa Yaafar Daher **m** *Consul General*
Mr Francisco J. Robayna *Political Attaché & Vice Consul*
Miss Anays Lisbeth Berrocal Corro *Representative to IMO*
Mr Luis Bernal Gonzalez **m** *Representative to IMO*

PAPUA NEW GUINEA

Papua New Guinea High Commission
14 Waterloo Place SW1Y 4AR
020 7930 0922
Fax 020 7930 0828
kunduldn3@btconnect.com
www.pnghighcomm.org.uk
Monday-Friday 09.00-17.00

HER EXCELLENCY MS WINNIE ANNA KIAP *High Commissioner (since 24 August 2011)*
Ms Judith Silau *1st Secretary*

PARAGUAY

Embassy of the Republic of Paraguay
3rd Floor 344 Kensington High Street W14 8NS
020 7610 4180
Fax 020 7371 4297
embaparuk@paraguayembassy.co.uk
embaparuk2@paraguayembassy.co.uk
www.paraguayembassy.co.uk
Monday-Friday 09.30-17.00

Consular Section
020 7610 4180
Fax 020 7371 4297
Monday-Friday 10.00-16.00

HIS EXCELLENCY MR GENARO VICENTE PAPPALARDO AYALA **m** *Ambassador Extraordinary & Plenipotentiary (since 31 March 2017)*
          Mrs Romina Araujo de Pappalardo
Mr Blas Alfredo Felip Himmelreich **m** *Counsellor*
Captain Luciano Roberto Picagua Villanueva **m** *Defence Attaché*
Mr Christian Olaf Heikel Ayala *Consular Attaché*

PERU

Embassy of Peru
52 Sloane Street SW1X 9SP
020 7235 1917/8340/3802
Fax 020 7235 4463
postmaster@peruembassy-uk.com
www.peruembassy-uk.com
Monday-Friday 09.00-17.00

Defence Attaché's Office
5 Fallstaff House, 24 Bardolph Road, Richmond TW9 2LH
020 8940 7773
Fax 020 8940 7735
peruattache@hotmail.com

Trade Office
5th Floor

One Knightsbridge Green
London SW1X 7NE
020 70528230
info@perutrade-uk.com

Consulate General
52 Sloane Street SW1X 9SP
020 7838 9223/9224
Fax 020 7823 2789
peruconsulate-uk@btconnect.com
Monday-Friday 09.30-13.00

HIS EXCELLENCY MR JUAN CARLOS GAMARRA **m** *Ambassador Extraordinary & Plenipotentiary & Permanent Representative to the IMO* (since 1 October 2018)
　　　　Mrs Désirée von Preussen de Gamarra
Mr Oswaldo Alfredo Del Aguila-Ramirez **m** *Minister & Deputy Head of Mission & Alternate Permanent Representative to the IMO*
Mrs. Roxana Castro Aranda de Bollig * *Minister (Consul General)*
Vice Admiral Francisco José Calisto-Giampietri **m** *Alternate Permanent Representative to the IMO*
Colonel Giovanni Antonio Contreras-Sevilla **m** *Deputy Defence & Military Attaché*
Colonel Richar Agustin Cano-Perez **m** *Police Attaché*
Mr José Antonio Pacheco-de Freitas **m** *Counsellor (Political Affairs)*
Mr Ricardo Leonardo Enrique Malca-Alvariño *Counsellor (Press and Cultural Affairs) and Alternate Permanent Representative to the IMO*
Mr Ricardo Eli Romero Talledo *Counsellor for Economic and Commercial Affairs*
Captain Edson Javier Fano-Espinoza **m** *Alternate Permanent Representative to the IMO*
Captain Ricardo Bernales-Meave **m** *Deputy Defence Attaché and Alternate Permanent Representative to the IMO*
Mr. Miguel Alejandro Ramírez Moscoso *1st Secretary (Deputy Consul)*
Major César Oswaldo Becerra-Salas **m** *Deputy Police Attaché*
Miss Cosette Israel Campos-Nieto *2nd Secretary (Economic & Investment Affairs)*

PHILIPPINES

Embassy of the Republic of the Philippines
6-11 Suffolk Street SW1Y 4HG
020 7451 1780
Fax: 020 7930 9787
embassy@philemb.co.uk
london.pe@dfa.gov.ph
http://londonpe.dfa.gov.ph
Monday-Friday 09.00-17.00

Consular Section: 020 7451 1803/1814/1815/1819
Political (Bilateral) Section: 020 7451 1806
Political (Multilateral) Section: 020 7451 1808
Cultural Section: 020 7451 1804
Economic Section: 020 7451 1812
Administration Section: 020 7451 1835

Labour & Welfare Section
3rd Floor, 6 Suffolk Street SW1Y 4HG
020 7839 8078/020 7451 1832
Fax 020 7839 7345
labattrdc59@yahoo.com

Defence & Armed Forces Section (Non-Resident)
Calle Guadalquivir, 6 28002 Madrid
0034 915 644 833/0034 917 823 830 (loc 817)
Fax 0034 915 644 833
phildafa90spain@yahoo.com

Trade Section

1a Cumberland House Kensington Court W8 5NX
020 7937 1898/7998
Fax 020 7937 2747
london@dti.gov.ph
london@philippinetrade.org
www.investphilippines.gov.ph

Tourism Section
2nd Floor, 10-11 Suffolk Street SW1Y 4HG
020 7321 0668
Fax 020 7925 2920
info@itsmorefuninthephilippines.co.uk

Maritime Section
3rd Floor, 10 Suffolk Street SW1Y 4HG
020 7839 1650
aflingad@marina.gov.ph

HIS EXCELLENCY MR ANTONIO MANUEL LAGDAMEO m *Ambassador Extraordinary and Plenipotentiary &*
Permanent Representative to the IMO (since 20 February 2017)
　　　　　Mrs Maria Linda Lagdameo
Mr Frank Cimafranca m *Deputy Chief of Mission*
Mr Senen Mangalile m *Deputy Chief of Mission, Consul General & Deputy Permanent Representative to the IMO*
Ms Arlene Gonzales-Macaisa * *Minister & Consul (Consular)*
Ms Rhenita Rodriguez *Minister & Consul (Political & Cultural))*
Ms Ana Marie Hernando *1st Secretary & Consul & Alternate Permanent Representative to the IMO*
Mr. Niño Anthony Balagtas m *2nd Secretary*
Ms Stacy Danika Alcantara-Garcia m *3rd Secretary & Vice Consul (Consular)*
Ms Beatriz Alexandra Martinez *3rd Secretary & Vice Consul (Administrative & Economic)*
Mr Neil Brillantes m *Attaché (Consular)*
Mr Eric Ricafort m *Attaché (Communications)*
Mr Douveylito Tangcay m *Attaché (Consular)*
Ms Maria Theresa Almirante m *Attaché (Administration)*
Ms Neriza Magaso * *Attaché (Consular)*
Mr Medardo Albano m *Attaché (Finance)*
Ms Maria Theresa Jesusa Albano m *Attaché (Administration)*
Ms Aleth Panopio m *Attaché (Consular)*
Ms Jehli Liggayu * *Attaché (Administration)*
Ms Rowena Ricafort m *Attaché (Consular)*
Ms Rosalyn del Valle Fajardo m *Attaché (Finance)*
Ms Mauro Fajardo III m *Attaché (Protocol)*
Ms Eleanor Regalado m *Attaché (Consular)*
Mr Ronald Allan Fernandez *Attaché (Consular)*
Ms Michelle Fatima Sanchez *Commercial Counsellor*
Ms Amuerfina Reyes * *Labour Attaché*
Mr Gerard Panga m *Tourism Attaché*
Ms Sonia Malaluan *Maritime Attaché*
Col Harold Anthony Pascua *INF (GSC) PA Defence Attaché (Non-Resident)*
Ms Maria Consolacion Marquez m *Welfare Officer*
Capt. Weniel Azcuna m *Technical Adviser to Maritime Attaché*

POLAND

Embassy of the Republic of Poland
47 Portland Place W1B 1JH
020 7291 3520
Fax 020 7291 3576
london@msz.gov.pl

www.london.mfa.gov.pl

Economic Section
Bravura House 10 Bouverie Street EC4Y 8AX
020 7822 8917
london.we@msz.gov.pl

Polish Cultural Institute
Bravura House 10 Bouverie Street EC4Y 8AX
020 7822 8990
Fax 020 7822 8951
pci@polishculture.org.uk
www.polishculture.org.uk

Consular Section
Bravura House 10 Bouverie Street EC4Y 8AX
020 7822 8900/1
Fax 020 7936 3571
londyn.konsulat@msz.gov.pl
www.london.mfa.gov.pl

HIS EXCELLENCY PROFESSOR ARKADY JÓZEF RZEGOCKI m *Ambassador Extraordinary & Plenipotentiary (since 30 August 2016)*
                Mrs Jolanta Rzegocka
Mrs Agnieszka Kowalska m *Deputy Head of Mission, First Counsellor*
Mr Mateusz Stąsiek m *Consul General, First Counsellor*
Colonel Mieczyslaw Malec * *Defence Attaché*
Colonel Norbert Marcin Czerbniak * *Deputy Defence Military, Naval & Air Attaché*
Lt Col Artur Miśkiewicz m *Deputy Defence Attaché*
Mrs Marta de Zuniga m *Minster-Counsellor (Deputy Director of the Polish Cultural Institute)*
Mr Mateusz Jozef Stasiek m *1st Counsellor/Consul General*
Ms Malgorzata Anna Buszynska *1st Counsellor/Permanent Representative to the IMO*
Mr Andrzej Kazimierz Krężel m *Counsellor (Head of Economic Section)*
Mrs Katarzyna Szaran m *3rd Secretary (Head of Media and Public Diplomacy)*
Mr Konrad Zielinski m *2nd Secretary (Deputy Director of the Polish Cultural Institute)*
Lt Col Bartosz Wojciech Furgała m *Counsellor (Liaison Officer of Polish Police)*
Mrs Izabella Irmina Gołaszewska-Mazek m *3rd Secretary (Head of Estates)*
Mr Mariusz Gasztoł m *Minister-Counsellor*
Mr Sylwester Lis m *Counsellor*
Mr Mirosław Kornacki m *Counsellor (Consular Affairs)*
Mrs Maja Żywioł m *Counsellor*
Ms Monika Anna Dobkowska *1st Secretary (Political)*
Ms Joanna Urszula Górzyńska *1st Secretary (Consular Affairs)*
Mrs Katarzyna Maria Hopkin m *1st Secretary (Consular Affairs)*
Mr Radoslaw Gromski m *2nd Secretary*
Mrs Maria Niesluchowska m *2nd Secretary (Consular Affairs*
Mr Tomasz Edward Polkowski m *2nd Secretary (IT Department)*
Mr Tomasz Wieslaw Balcerowski m *2nd Secretary/Vice-Consul*
Mr Krzysztof Adam Zieliński m *2nd Secretary (Political)*
Ms Dorota Maria Śpiewak *3rd Secretary (Vice Consul)*
Ms Martyna Lesica *3rd Secretary (Consular Affairs)*
Mr Szymon Mieszko Szaran m *3rd Secretary (Political)*
Mrs Katarzyna Szaran m *3rd Secretary (Head of Media and Public Diplomacy)*
Miss Paulina Izabela Stepień *Head of Finanace*
Mrs Beata Jadwiga Sudar m *3rd Secretary*
Mr Arkadiusz Marek Cygan m *3rd Secretary (Economic)*
Mr Krzysztof Stolarczyk * *Warrant Officer*

PORTUGAL

Embassy of Portugal
11 Belgrave Square SW1X 8PP

020 7235 5331
Fax 020 7235 0739
londres@mne.pt

Trade & Tourism
020 7201 6666
Fax 020 7201 6633
trade.london@portugalglobal.pt
tourism.london@portugalglobal.pt

Consulate General
3 Portland Place W1B 1HR
020 7291 3770
Fax 020 7291 3799
consulado.londres@mne.pt

HIS EXCELLENCY MR MANUEL LOBO ANTUNES **m** *Ambassador Extraordinary & Plenipotentiary (since 2 September 2016)*
      Mrs Maria Plantier Santos Lobo Antunes
Mr Antonio Jose Marques Sabido Costa **m** *Minister-Counsellor,*
Mrs Cristina Maria Cerqueira Pucarinho **m** *Consul General*
Mr João de Brito *Deputy Consul General*
Mr João Nuno Sousa de Albuquerque *1st Secretary*
Mr Pedro de Moraes Sarmento Patrício *Counsellor (Economic & Commercial)*
Ms Helena Paula de Sousa e Silva Fernandes *Press Attaché*
Ms Cláudia Cristina Marques Miguel *Attaché (Tourism)*
Dr Regina Duarte *Attaché (Educational Affairs)*
Mrs Maria Joao Leal da Silva Freire Morgado *Attaché (Legal Affairs)*
Ms Ana Paula Prazeres de Almeida *Attaché (Tourism PR and Press)*

QATAR

Embassy of the State of Qatar
1 South Audley Street W1K 1NB
020 7493 2200
Fax 020 7493 2661
Monday-Friday 09.30-16.00
amb@qatarembassy.org.uk
amblondon@mofa.gov.qa

Cultural Section
47 Park Lane W1K 1PR
020 8076 1111
Fax 0208 076 1413
secretary-uk@edu.gov.qa

Medical Section
30 Collingham Gardens, London, SW5 0HN
020 7370 6871
Fax 020 7835 1469
qatmeduk@qatarhealth.co.uk

Military Section
21 Hertford Street W1J 7RY
020 7409 2229
Fax 020 7629 0740
mfahmi@qda.qa

HIS EXCELLENCY MR YOUSEF ALI AL-KHATER **m** *Ambassador Extraordinary & Plenipotentiary (since 23 October 2014)*
      Mrs Maryam R Y Al-Khater
Mr Hamad Bin Khalifa Bin Hamad Al-Thani **m** *Minister-Counsellor*
Mr Hamad Bin Jassim J M Al-Thani **m** *Minister-Counsellor*

Mr Mohamed Abdulla Al-Jabir **m** *Minister (Deputy Head of Mission)*
Brigadier Hamad Almarri **m** *Defence Attache*
Mr Ali Saleh Al-Fadhala * *Counsellor*
Mr Jassim Al-Moftah **m** *First Secretary*
Mr Ghanim Abdulrahman Al-Hodaifi Al-Kuwari **m** *Second Secretary*
Mr Salman Jassim Al- Thani **m** *Second Secretary*
Mr Abdulrahman Mohamed Al-Baker * *Second Secretary-Consul*
Mr Matar Al-Kuwari **m** *Second Secretary*
Miss Sara Al-Saadi *Second Secretary*
Mr Nasser Jassim Al-Thani **m** *Attaché*
Sheikh Thamer Hamad Al-Thani **m** *Communications Attaché*
Mr Abdulla Al-Ghanim *Commercial Attache*
Staff Brigadier Ali Abdulla Ghorab Al-Marri **m** *Assistant Defence Attaché*
Col. Nawaf Al-Naimi **m** *Assistant Naval Attaché*
Mr Mohammed Rashid Al-Kuwari * *First Secretary/ Military Students Affairs*
Ms Ameena Salman Al-Meer *1st Secretary (Senior Academic Adviser)*
Dr Mohamed Abdulla Al-Kaabi **m** *Cultural Attaché*
Mr Fahad Al-Kuwari **m** *Assistant Cultural Attaché*

ROMANIA

Embassy of Romania
Arundel House 4 Palace Green W8 4QD
Phone : 020 7937 9666
Fax 020 7937 8069
londra@mae.ro
www.londra.mae.ro
Monday-Friday 09.00-17.00

Consular Section - London
M.E.I.C. House 344 Kensington High Street W14 8NS
Phone: 020 7602 9833
Fax 020 7602 4229
londra.cons@mae.ro

Commercial Section
Arundel House 4 Palace Green W8 4QD
Phone: 020 7937 9668
Fax 020 7937 8069
londra.economic@mae.ro

Defence Attaché's Office
Arundel House 4 Palace Green W8 4QD
Phone : 020 7937 4379
Fax 020 7937 4379
londra.aparare@mae.ro

Home Affairs Attaché's Office
Arundel House 4 Palace Green W8 4QD
Phone : 02079379666
Fax : 02079378069
londra.mai@mae.ro

Labour and Social Affairs Attaché's Office
Arundel House 4 Palace Green, London W8 4QD
Phone : 020 7937 8125
Fax:020 7937 8069
londra.social@mae.ro

Romanian Cultural Institute
1 Belgrave Square SW1X 8PH
Phone : 020 7752 0134
Fax 020 7235 0383

office@icr-london.co.uk
www.icr-london.co.uk

His Excellency MR SORIN-DAN MIHALACHE m *Ambassador Extraordinary & Plenipotentiary (since 21 June 2016)*
    Mrs Mădălina Beatrice Mihalache
Mrs Daniela Laura Popescu * *Minister Plenipotentiary (Deputy Head of Mission)*
Mr Daniel Robert Adrian Marin m *Minister Plenipotentiary (Political and Consular)*
Mr Alexandru Dodan m *Minister-Counsellor*
Mrs Mary-Eliana Teodorescu *Minister-Counsellor (Political)*
Mr Valentin Ciprian Muntean m *Consul General (Head of Consular Section London)*
Mrs Elena-Violeta Stoica m *Minister Counsellor*
Mrs Alina Popescu m *Minister Counsellor (Political)*
Mrs Gilda Luiza Truică m *Minister Counsellor*
Mr Sebastian-Constantin Ezaru m *Defence Military Air and Naval Attaché*
Navy Captain Marian Stan m *Deputy Defence Attaché*
Mrs Mădălina Sorina Vlangăr m *Counsellor (Home Affairs Attaché)*
Mrs Andra-Caterina Popescu m *Counsellor*
Mr Bogdan George Văduva m *1st Secretary (Commercial Section)*
Ms Mihaela Enache *1st Secretary*
Mr Gheorghiță-Florin Ciornei m *2nd Secretary*
Ms Amalia Irina Pufulescu *3rd Secretary*
Mr Vlad Vida m *Counsellor (Deputy Home Affairs Attaché)*
Ms Rodica-Andreea Cărăuşu *Social& Labour Affairs Attaché*
Mrs Camelia Oprescu *Consul General*
Mr Valentin Macec m *Consul*

RUSSIA

Embassy of the Russian Federation (Residence of the Ambassador)
13 Kensington Palace Gardens, London, W8 4QX
0207 229 3620
0207 229 7281
Fax 0207 229 5804

Embassy of the Russian Federation (Main Building)
6/7 Kensington Palace Gardens, London, W8 4QP
0207 229 6412
Fax 0207 727 8625
kanc@rusemb.org.uk
www.rusemb.org.uk

Consular Department
5 Kensington Palace Gardens, London W8 4QS
0203 668 7474
www.rusemb.org.uk/consulate
info@rusemb.org.uk

Defence Attaché's Office
44 Millfield Lane N6 6JB
0208 341 7979
Fax 0208 341 7744

Office of the Trade Representative
33 Highgate West Hill N6 6NL
0208 340 1907
Fax 0208 348 0112
www.rustrade.org.uk

HIS EXCELLENCY ANDREI KELIN *Ambassador Extraordinary & Plenipotentiary (since 21 November 2019)*
    Mrs Irina Kelina
Mr Ivan Volodin m *Minister-Counsellor*
Mr Boris Abramov m *Trade Representative*
Colonel Mikhail Ivanov m *Defence Attaché*

Mr Igor Vinokurov **m** *Senior Counsellor*
Mr Denis Piminov **m** *Senior Counsellor*
Mr Vladimir Derbenskiy **m** *Counsellor*
Mr Murad Nasrutdinov **m** *Counsellor (Deputy Representative to IMO)*
Mrs Olga Zykova **m** *Counsellor*
Mr Kirill Sokolov-Shsherbachev **m** *Counsellor (Head of Consular Section)*
Mr Gennady Antonov **m** *Counsellor*
Mr Maxim Sizov **m** *Counsellor*
Mr Stanislav Antipin *1st Secretary*
Mr Ilya Erofeev **m** *1st Secretary*
Mrs Ksenia Verkholantseva **m** *1st Secretary*
Mr Arsen Daduani **m** *1st Secretary*
Mr Yury Boychenko **m** *1st Secretary*
Mr Sergey Fedichkin **m** *2nd Secretary*
Mr Konstantin Yushmanov **m** *2nd Secretary*
Mr Ilya Tolstykh **m** *2nd Secretary*
Mr Stepan Anikeev **m** *2nd Secretary*
Mr Vadim Retyunskiy *3rd Secretary*
Mr Kirill Matrenichev **m** *3rd Secretary*
Mr Roman Balashov **m** *3rd Secretary*
Mr Kirill Gruzdev **m** *3rd Secretary*
Mr Andrey Bugaets **m** *3rd Secretary*
Mr Aleksandr Iarovoi *3rd Secretary*
Ms Mariam Semenova *3rd Secretary*
Mr Ivan Gozhev **m** *3rd Secretary*
Ms Nina Mishchenko *3rd Secretary*
Mr Dmitry Golubovskiy **m** *3rd Secretary*
Mrs Anastasia Erofeeva **m** *3rd Secretary*
Mr Igor Pavlov *3rd Secretary*
Mr Nikolai Shurulia **m** *Attaché*
Mr Riias Komarov **m** *Attaché*
Mr Mikhail Ikonnikov **m** *Attaché*
Mr Roman Yudanov **m** *Attaché*
Mr Viacheslav Polevoi **m** *Attaché*
Mr Dmitry Ananiev **m** *Attaché*
Mr Aleksandr Soin **m** *Attaché*
Ms Elena Marchan *Attaché*
Ms Natalia Zatulko *Attaché*
Mr Alexander Trubachev **m** *Attaché*
Mr Baslan Abdullaev **m** *Attaché*
Mr Evgeny Kiselev **m** *Attaché*

RWANDA

Rwanda High Commission
120-122 Seymour Place
London
W1H 1NR
020 7224 9832
Fax: 020 7724 8642
Email:uk@rwandahc.org
www.rwandahc.org

HER EXCELLENCY MS YAMINA CLARIS KARITANYI *High Commissioner (since 9 January 2016)*
Mr Fidelis Mironko **m** *1st Counsellor*
Mr James Wizeye **m** *1st Secretary*

SAINT CHRISTOPHER & NEVIS

High Commission for Saint Christopher & Nevis
10 Kensington Court W8 5DL
020 7937 9718

Fax 020 937 7484
mission@sknhc.co.uk
www.stkittsnevishcuk.gov.kn

HIS EXCELLENCY DR KEVIN M. ISAAC m *High Commissioner (since 12 January 2011)*
        Mrs Prangtip Isaac
Mrs Elsa G. Wilkin-Armbrister m *Minister-Counsellor (Investment and Further Development)*
Mr Gurdip Bath m *Commercial Attaché (Business & Trade)*

SAINT LUCIA

High Commission for Saint Lucia
1 Collingham Gardens SW5 0HW
020 7370 7123
Fax 020 7370 1905
enquiries@stluciahcuk.org

MR GUY MAYERS m *High Commissioner (since 17 December 2016)*
        Mrs Hannah Ruth Mayers
Mrs Leonne Theodore-John * *Minister-Counsellor*
Mr Enrico Louis Monfrini Counsellor (Economic)
Mrs Rose-Anne Evelyn-Bates m *1st Secretary (Political)*
Mrs Veronica Francis-Joseph * *Vice Consul*

SAINT VINCENT & THE GRENADINES

High Commission for Saint Vincent & the Grenadines
10 Kensington Court W8 5DL
020 7460 1256
020 7565 2874
Fax 020 7937 6040
info@svghighcom.co.uk
www.svghighcom.co.uk
www.gov.vc

High Commissioner's Office
020 7565 2874
office@svghighcom.co.uk

Political & Commercial Section
020 7565 2885
mc@svghighcom.co.uk

Consular Section
020 7460 2588
info@svghighcom.co.uk

HIS EXCELLENCY MR CENIO E. LEWIS m *High Commissioner (since 24 April 2001)*
        Mrs Ita Lewis
Miss Jinelle Kinique Adams *Minister Counsellor*
Mrs Carolin De Freitas-Sawh m *Counsellor*

SAMOA

High Commission of the Independent State of Samoa
Avenue Commandant Lothaire 1, 1040 Brussels
+32 2 660 8454
Fax +32 2 675 0336
samoaembassy@skynet.be

HIS EXCELLENCY FATUMANAVA DR PAOLELEI LUTERU m *High Commissioner (since 14 August 2012)*
Ms Theresa Penn m *Counsellor*
Ms Maxine Hunter *First Secretary*

SAN MARINO

Embassy of the Republic of San Marino
All correspondence should be addressed to the Department of Foreign Affairs
Palazzo Begni – Contrada Omerelli 47890 San Marino – Republic of San Marino
+378 (0549) 882422
Fax +378 (0549) 992018
dipartimentoaffariesteri@pa.sm

HER EXCELLENCY DR SILVIA MARCHETTI *Ambassador Extraordinary & Plenipotentiary* (since 25 September 2018)

SÃO TOMÉ & PRINCIPE

Embassy of São Tomé & Principe
175 Avenue de Tervuren 1150 Brussels
00322 734 8966
Fax 00322 734 8815
Ambassade@saotomeeprincipe.be

London Honorary Consulate (see Honorary Consuls section below)

Vacant *Ambassador Extraordinary & Plenipotentiary*
Mr Armindo de Brito m *Chargé d'Affaires a.i.*
Mr Horatio Fernando da Forseca m *2nd Secretary*

SAUDI ARABIA

Royal Embassy of Saudi Arabia
30 Charles Street, Mayfair W1J 5DZ.
020 7917 3000

Defence Attaché's Office
26 Queens Gate, SW7 5JE
020 7581 7070

Diplomatic Office of the Cultural Bureau
630 Chiswick High Road, London W4 5RY
020 3249 7000

Medical Section
Building 3, Cheswick Park
Cheswick High Road, W4 5YA
020 8863 2200

Consular Office
32 Charles Street, Mayfair W1J 5DZ
020 7917 3000

Economic Section
30 Charles Street, Mayfair W1J 5DZ
020 7917 3000

Commercial Section
15/16 Queens Street, Mayfair W1J 5PQ
020 7723 7817

Islamic Affairs Section
2nd Floor Park Lorne, 111 Park Road NW8 7JL
020 7723 7817

Information Section
18 Seymour Street, London W1H 7HU
020 7486 8324

HIS EXCELLENCY HRH Prince Khalid Bin Bandar Bin Sultan Al-Saud **m** *Ambassador Extraordinary & Plenipotentiary (since 01 July 2019)*
      HH Princess Lucy Caroline Al-Saud
Mr Saud N H Al Hamdan **m** *Minister Plenipotentiary (Deputy Head of Mission)*
H H Prince Sultan Fahad Abdullah Al-Saud **m** *Minister Plenipotentiary*
Mr Abdullah Zayed Assiri **m** *Counsellor*
Mr Bander Fahad A. Al-Zaid **m** *Counsellor (Head of the Consulate)*
Mr Ahmed Saleh A Al Shehri **m** *Counsellor (Head of Administration & Communication Department)*
Mr Khalid Abdullah A Al-Rajhi **m** *Counsellor*
Mr Sulaiman Mohammed S Al Anbar *Counsellor*
Mr Abdullah Mohamad A Al Hamdan **m** *1st Secretary*
Mr Khalid Omar m Basfar **m** *1st Secretary*
Mr Talal Ghormullah Al-Ghamdi **m** *1st Secretary*
Miss Hend Ibrahim S Al Ibrahim *1st Secretary*
Mr Khaled Abdallh I Al Gaffis **m** *1st Secretary*
Mr Saleh Mohamed S Al Daham *1st Secretary*
Mr Hassan Mohamed Al Ahmari **m** *1st Secretary*
Mr Ammar Fahad I Al Ammar **m** *1st Secretary*
Mr Ahmed Abdullah Al Hamaidi **m** *2nd Secretary*
Mr Fahad Mansour KH Ben Garmalah **m** *2nd Secretary*
Mr Khalid Hamed M Bakhsh *2nd Secretary*
Ms Jamila Haif Al-Khatani *2nd Secretary*
Mr Abdullah Abdulaziz Al-Hoshan **m** *2nd Secretary*
H.H Prince Sultan Bin Jalawi A. Bin Mousaad Al Saud *3rd Secretary*
Miss Jomana Rashed F. Al Rashid *3rd Secretary*
Miss Selma Khalid M. Jaber *3rd Secretary*
Mr Shakir Hassan A Al Sharif *3rd Secretary*
Mr Abdullah Mohammed S Al Qarni **m** *3rd Secretary*
Mr Faisal Saad Al-Sheraimy **m** *3rd Secretary*
Mr Mohammed Shajaan A. Al Ogaili * *3rd Secretary*
Mr Waleed Suleiman KH Al-Natheer **m** *3rd Secretary*
Mr Hatem Abo Gamel **m** *3rd Secretary*
Mr Tarek Mohammed N Al Nashmi *3rd Secretary*
Mr Fawaz Ali S Al Maiman **m** *3rd Secretary*
Mr Sultan Rashed M. Al Shehri *3rd Secretary*
Mr Mouath Saeed Al Ghamdi *3rd Secretary*
Mr Abdulrahman Mohammed Al Fwzan **m** *3rd Secretary*
Mr Abdullah Yousif A Al Saadi *3rd Secretary*
Mr Abdulrahman Jamal A Al Jama **m** *3rd Secretary*
Mr Abdullah Yousel Al Khalaf **m** *3rd Secretary*
Mr Naif Hussain M Tami **m** *3rd Secretary*
Mr Abdulaziz Aladham A Al Onazi **m** *Attaché*
Miss Njoud Zaid T Al Khudairy *Attaché*
Mr Nawaf Faiez Y Al Thari *Attaché*
Mr Bader H.A. Al-Harpi **m** *Attaché*
Mr Fahad Abdulrahman A. Al Muhaya *Attaché*
Mr Mushref Abdullah S. Al Amri **m** *Attaché*
Mr Thamer Mohammed A. Al Akeel **m** *Attaché*
Mr Mohammed Mansour H Al Mahyoubi *Attaché*
Mr Waleed Awad A Al Awad **m** *Attaché (Communications Department)*
Brig General Riyadh Mohammed A. Aboabat **m** *Defence Attache*
Lt Col Bandaer Hamid S Ahmed **m** *Assistant Attaché*
Col Pilot Mohammed Othman A. Al-Jaloud **m** *Air & Assistant Military Attaché (Airforce Affairs)*
Col Pilot Badr Abdulrahman F Al Mubarak **m** *Training Manager (Airforce Affairs)*
Col Bandar Mohammed B Oraier **m** *Attaché (Defence)*

Col Khaled Saleh A Al Turki m *Attaché (Defence)*
Lt Col Ahmed Abu Hadi m *Administrative Attaché*
Commander Abdullah Ayedh Al Harbi m *Attaché (Defence)*
Lt Commander Zakariya Abdullah M Al-Said m *Attaché (Defence)*
Mr Loai Abdulaziz F Al Fraih m *Attaché (Defence)*
Major Ahmad Ali A Al Assiri m *Attaché (Defence)*
Major Ibrahim Hamad I Bin Masoud * *Attaché (Defence)*
HRH Prince Abdulaziz Bin Saif Alnasr Bin Saud Bin Abdulaziz Al Saud m *Attaché (Defence)*
Lieutenant Muhannad Moneer M Al-Fakhrani m *Attaché (Defence)*
Mr Omar Hammad O. Al-Ghofaili m *Attaché (Head of Accounts Department)*
Mr Abdulaziz Hamad S Al Suwilem m *Attache (Defence)*
Mr Saud Khalf M Al Anazi m *Attaché (Defence)*
Mr Abdullah Mohammed Al Jumaah m *Attaché (Acting Cultural Attache)*
Dr Adel Abdulrahman Al-Yobi m *Attaché (Cultural)*
Dr Abdulaziz Saleh Al-Raddadi m *Attaché (Cultural Office Academic Advisor)*
Dr Talal Ghazi N Al-Harbi m *Attaché (Cultural Office Academic Advisor)*
Dr Faisal Mohammad A Al Shareef m *Attaché (Cultural)*
Dr Madallah AlRokwi M Al Enazi m *Attaché (Cultural)*
Dr Mohammad Othman M AbaHussin m *Attaché (Cultural)*
Mr Mohammed Ali Al Lohidan m *Attaché (Cultural)*
Mr Abdullah Ibrahim M Al Othman * *Attaché (Cultural)*
Mr Abdullah Abdulrahman A Bin Saeedan m *Attaché (Cultural)*
Mr Khalid Abdulrahman Al Yousef m *Attaché (Cultural)*
Mr Abdullah Hamad M Al Anazi m *Attaché (Cultural)*
Mr Abdulaziz Zaid A. Al-Zaid m *Attaché (Cultural)*
Mr Abdulaziz Mohamad N. Al Mohaya m *Attaché (Cultural)*
Mr Bader Saeed O Al Omar m *Attaché (Cultural)*
Mr Abdullah Mohammad A Al Mohaimeed m *Attaché (Head of Information Office)*
Mr Majed Hadi Al Kahtani m *Attaché (Information Office)*
Mr Hamdan Nawar A Al Otaibi m *Attaché (Commercial Office)*
Dr Abdulaziz Mohamed Al-Eisa m *Attaché Director of the Health Office*
Dr Ibraheem Khalifa Al Hanout m *Assistant to the Health Attaché*
Mr Ahmed Brjes G Al Otaibi m *Attaché (Health Office)*
Dr Ahmed Al-Dubayan m *Attaché (Islamic Affairs)*
Dr Mohammed Ahmed F Al Faifi m *Attaché (Islamic Affairs)*
Mr Mansour Abdullah M Al-Aql m *Attaché*
Mr Ali F M Al-Omran m *Attaché*
Mr Saleh Abdullah S. Alshethri m *Attaché (Director of Internal Security)*
Mr Ali Ahmed O Al Sharif * *Attaché (Deputy Head, Embassy Security)*
Brig. Gen. Hussain S Al-Kahtani m *Assistant Defence Attaché (Air)*

SENEGAL

Embassy of the Republic of Senegal
39 Marloes Road W8 6LA
Tel: 020 7938 4048 / 020 7937 7237
Fax 020 7938 2546
senegalembassy@hotmail.co.uk
www.senegalembassy.com

HER EXCELLENCY DR FATIMATA DIA m *Ambassador Extraordinary & Plenipotentiary (since 29 November 2019)*
        Mr Nouhamadou Falilou Diague
Mr Aliou Diallo m *1st Counsellor*
Mr Dramane Samoura m *2nd Counsellor*
Mrs Collette Thiakane Faye m 2nd *Counsellor*
Mr Papa Cheikh Sylla m *1st Secretary*
Mr Ibrahima Sall m *1st Secretary*
Mr El Hadji Cheikh Diop m *1st Secretary*
Mrs Rokhaya Samb m *2nd Secretary*

SERBIA

Embassy of the Republic of Serbia
28 Belgrave Square SW1X 8QB
Tel: 020 7235 9049
Fax:020 7235 7092
london@serbianembassy.org.uk
www.london.mfa.gov.rs

HER EXCELLENCY MRS ALEKSANDRA JOKSIMOVIĆ **m** *Ambassador Extraordinary & Plenipotentiary (since 1 December 2018)*
      Mr Siniša Krajčinović
Mr Vladimir Dišović *Counsellor*
Mrs Neda Mijajlović * *Counsellor*
Miss Marijana Ognjanović *Counsellor (Consular Affairs)*
Mr Veljko Jelenković **m** *2nd Secretary*
Mrs Stana Vučković **m** *Attaché*
Captain (Navy) Slobodan Novaković **m** *Defence Attaché*
Lt Colonel Ilija Vujičić **m** *Assistant Defence Attaché*

SEYCHELLES

The High Commission of the Republic of Seychelles
130-132 Buckingham Palace Road SW1W 9SA
Tel: 020 7730 2046
office@seychelleshcl.co.uk
Monday-Friday 09.00-17.00

Consular Section
020 7730 2046
079 58433 877 (Emergency)

Commercial Section
020 7730 0700
seychelles@uksto.co.uk
www.seychelles.travel
Monday-Friday 09.00-17.00

HIS EXCELLENCY MR DERICK ALLY *High Commissioner (since 25 January 2017)*
Mr Terry Romain Principal *Counsellor*
Ms Christine Vel *Commercial Attaché*

SIERRA LEONE

Sierra Leone High Commission
41 Eagle Street WC1R 4TL
020 7404 0140
Fax 020 7430 9862
info@slhc-uk.org.uk
www.slhc-uk.org.uk
Monday-Friday 09.30-13.00 & 14.00-17.00

HIS EXCELLENCY DR MORIE KOMBA MANYEH * *High Commissioner (since 15 October 2019)*
Mrs Agnes Kumba Dugba Macauley **m** *Deputy High Commissioner*
Mr Alan C Logan **m** *Head of Chancery*
Mr Christopher Bockarie **m** *Counsellor*
Mrs Clara Koroma * *Counsellor*
Mrs Kebiatu Modu-Kamara **m** *2nd Secretary*
Mr John Ellie **m** *Financial Attaché*
Mr Festus A Kuyembeh **m** *Financial Attaché*

SINGAPORE

High Commission for the Republic of Singapore
9 Wilton Crescent, London SW1X 8SP
020 7235 8315
Fax 020 7245 6583
singhc_lon@mfa.sg
http://mfa.gov.sg/london
Monday-Friday 09.00-17.00

Consular Section
Basement 9 Wilton Crescent, London SW1X 8SP
020 7235 8315
Fax 020 7235 9850
singhc_con_lon@mfa.sg
Monday-Friday 09.30-12.30

Liaison Office
Office No 214, 239 High Street Kensington, London W8 6SN
020 7960 6655 & 020 7960 6656

Commercial Section
Singapore Centre First Floor, Southwest House, 11A Regent Street, London SW1Y 4LR
020 7484 2730
http://www.iesingapore.gov.sg

Maritime Section
Singapore Centre First Floor, Southwest House, 11A Regent Street, London SW1Y 4LR
020 7484 2738

HER EXCELLENCY MS FOO CHI HSIA *High Commissioner (since 1 September 2014)*
Ms Rozana Binte Abdul Majid * *Deputy High Commissioner & Counsellor*
Mr Peter Mok Eck Piang **m** *Counsellor (Liaison Office)*
Mr Kum Cheong Aw **m** *Counsellor (Security Liaison)*
Mr Isaac Chan *1st Secretary (Political)*
Mr Vishnuvarthan *Balakrishnan* **m** *1st Secretary (Admin & Consular)*
Mr Hanqiang Tan **m** *1st Secretary (Maritime)*
Mr Samuel Soo Zi Hua *1st Secretary (Maritime)*
Ms Ang Hui Teng **m** *1st Secretary (Commercial)*
Ms Zhang Yufang Jane **m** *1st Secretary*
Mr Lau Yu Chin Leon *2nd Secretary*
Mr Koh Chong Hau * *Attaché*
Ms Celest Yin Hsien Chang * *Attaché (Admin & Technical)*

SLOVAKIA

Embassy of Slovakia
25 Kensington Palace Gardens W8 4QY
Tel 020 7313 6470
Tel 020 7313 6471 Ambassador's Office
Fax 020 7313 6481
emb.london@mzv.sk
www.mzv.sk/londyn
Monday-Thursday 08.30-16.45
Friday 08.30-15.30

Consular & Visa Section
cons.london@mzv.sk
Monday-Tuesday 09.00-12.00 & 13.00-16.00
Wednesday 10.00-13.00 & 14.00-18.00
Thursday 09.00-12.00 & 13.00-16.00
Friday 09.00-12.00

Defence Attaché's Office
Tel/Fax 020 7792 0215

HIS EXCELLENCY MR LUBOMÍR REHÁK **m** *Ambassador Extraordinary & Plenipotentiary (since 10 August 2015)*
        Mrs Dana Reháková
Mr Marcel Babicz **m** *Counsellor, Deputy Head of Mission*
Colonel Jan Goceliak **m** *Defence Attaché*
Mr Roman Mockovčák **m** *Counsellor*
Ms Elena Mallicková *Counsellor (Cultural)*
Mr Michal Horvat **m** *1st Secretary (Economic)*
Ms Andrea Stromčeková *1st Secretary*
Mr Marek Murín * *1st Secretary, Head of Consular Section*
Ms Kristina Szabová *2nd Secretary (Economic)*
Mrs Marcela Matúšková * *3rd Secretary (Consular)*
Ms Klaudia Volnerová *3rd Secretary (Consular)*
Mr Jozef Čurgaly *Attaché (Administrative)*
Mr Róbert Reháček **m** *Attaché (Administrative)*
Mr Milan Matlovič *Attaché (Political, Protocol)*

SLOVENIA

Embassy of the Republic of Slovenia
17 Dartmouth Street
London SW1H 9BL
Tel.: 020 7222 5700
sloembassy.london@gov.si
www.london.embassy.si

Consular Section
Tel.: 020 7227 9711
E-mail:consular.london@gov.si
Monday 10:00 – 13:00, Wednesday 10:00 – 13:00, 14:00 -16:00 Thursday 10:00 – 13:00

HIS EXCELLENCY MR TADEJ RUPEL **m** *Ambassador Extraordinary & Plenipotentiary* (since 14 August 2014)
        Mrs Valentina Prevolnik Rupel, PhD
Mrs Darja Golež **m** *Minister Plenipotentiary, Deputy Head of Mission*
Mrs Katja Biloslav **m** *Minister Plenipotentiary - Consul*
Ms Darja Slokar, *Minister Plenipotentiary (Economics)*
Mr Miha Fatur *First Counsellor (Political Affairs)*

SOLOMON ISLANDS

High Commission for the Solomon Islands
Room 1819
Portland House
Bressenden Place
London
SW1E 5RS

HIS EXCELLENCY MR ELIAM TANGIRONGO **m** *High Commissioner (Since 19 September 2018)*
        Mrs Anna Tangirongo
Mrs Clera Waokea Rotu **m** *2nd Secretary (Political)*

SOMALIA
No official Embassy address at present time
Vacant *Ambassador Extraordinary & Plenipotentiary*

SOUTH AFRICA
High Commission of the Republic of South Africa

South Africa House
Trafalgar Square WC2N 5DP
020 7451 7299
Fax 020 7839 5670
london.sahc@dirco.gov.za
London.info@dirco.gov.za

Home Affairs Section
15 Whitehall
SW1A 2DD
020 7925 89800/01
Fax 020 7839 5198
london.civic@dirco.gov.za
london.visa@dirco.gov.za

HER EXCELLENCY MS NOMATEMBA GUGULETHU PUDNIXIA OLIVIA TAMBO *High Commissioner*
Mr Ronald Sipho Jama Mbatha **m** *Minister (Transport)*
Brig-Gen Edward Ramabu **m** *Defence Adviser*
Ms Rasheeda Adam *Counsellor (Political)*
Ms Elizabeth Nkone Aphane *Counsellor (Immigration & Civic Services)*
Mr Marc Jürgens **m** *Counsellor (Political)*
Mrs Mogomotsi Vinolia Makwetla **m** *Counsellor (ICT)*
Col Phineas Vusimuzi Mpela **m** *Deputy Defence Adviser*
Mr Pubudu Kenneth Mahlake **m** *First Secretary (ICT)*
Mrs Jenny Mcube **m** *First Secretary (Corporate Services)*
Mr Mpho Comfort Moloto *First Secretary* (ICT)
Ms Tshepiso Emmah Kube *Second Secretary* (Immigration and Civic Services)
Mr Ramoshoane Adam Sethosa **m** *Second Secretary* (Immigration and Civic Services)
Mr Sibusiso Ntando Maseko **m** *Third Secretary* (Corporate Services)
Ms Prudence Mabena *Third Secretary* (Corporate Services)
WO1 Nompumelelo Carol Radebe * *Defence Office Chief Clerk*

SOUTH SUDAN

Embassy of the Republic of South Sudan
22-25 Portman Close, W1H 6BS
020 36872366
info@embrss.org.uk
www.embrss.org.uk

Vacant *Ambassador Extraordinary & Plenipotentiary*
Mrs Ashwil Haruun Lual Ruun * *Chargé d' Affaires a.i*
Mr Maker Ayuel Deng **m** *Minister Plenipotentiary*
Brigadier General Charles Malet Kuol * *Defence Attaché*
Mr Majak Arop Kuol Arop **m** *Counsellor*
Mr George Isaac Kut Guj *3rd Secretary*
Mr Giir Giir Majok Biar * *Immigration Attaché*
Mr Majong Kau Dut *Immigration Officer*

SPAIN

Embassy of Spain
39 Chesham Place SW1X 8SB
020 7235 5555
Fax 020 7259 5392
emb.londres@maec.es
www.exteriores.gob.es/Embajadas/londres/en
@EmbSpainUK

Consulate General
20 Draycott Place SW3 2RZ
020 7589 8989
0871 376 0023 (Visa Information)

Fax 020 7581 7888
cog.londres@maec.es
www.exteriores.gob.es/Consulados/londres/en

Cultural Office
39 Chesham Place SW1X 8SB
020 7201 5517/5522/5524
Fax 020 7259 6487
emb.londres.ofc@maec.es

Defence Office
1st Floor, 20 Peel Street W8 7PD
020 7313 9078
Fax 020 7792 4570
agredlon@oc.mde.es

Transport Office - Permanent Representation to the International Maritime Organization
39 Chesham Place SW1X 8SB
020 7201 5539
Fax 020 7235 9303
imo.spain@fomento.es

Education Office
20 Peel Street W8 7PD
020 7727 2462
Fax 020 7229 4965
info.uk@educacion.gob.es
www.educacion.gob.es/reinounido

Employment, Migrations & Social Security Office
20 Peel Street W8 7PD
020 7221 0098 / 020 7243 9897
Fax 020 7229 7270
reinounido@mitramiss.es
www.empleo.gob.es

Economic & Commercial Office
125 Old Broad Street EC2N 1AR
020 7776 7730
Fax 020 7374 8896
londres@comercio.mineco.es

Agriculture, Fisheries & Food Office
39 Chesham Place SW1X 8SB
020 7235 5005
Fax 020 7259 6897
londres@mapama.es

Press & Communications Office
39 Chesham Place SW1X 8SB
020 7235 7537
Fax 020 7235 2263
londres@comunicacion.presidencia.gob.es

Liaison Magistrate Unit
39 Chesham Place SW1X 8SB
020 7235 5555
Fax 020 7259 5392
enlace.reinounido@justicia.es

HIS EXCELLENCY MR CARLOS BASTARRECHE SAGÜES **m** *Ambassador Extraordinary & Plenipotentiary (since 1 March 2017)*

Mrs Rosalía Gomez-Pineda
Mr José M. Fernández Lòpez de Turiso *Minister Counsellor, Deputy Head of Mission*
Mr Carlos Díaz Valcarcel **m** *Consul General*
Colonel (Marine Corps) Fernando Cayetano Garrido **m** *Defence, Naval, Army & Air Attaché*
Mr Miguel Oliveros Torres *Counsellor for Cultural & Scientific Affairs*
Mrs María Cruz-Guzman Flores *Counsellor*
Mrs Ana M. Rodríguez Pérez * *Counsellor (Press & Communications)*
Ms Soledad García López *Counsellor (Customs, Excise & Tax Affairs)*
Mr Felix J. Alvarez Saavedra * *Counsellor (Home Affairs)*
Mr Victor Jiménez Fernandez **m** *Counsellor (Transport & Maritime Affairs)*
Mr Gonzalo Capellán de Miguel **m** *Counsellor (Education)*
Mrs Reyes Zataraín Del Valle **m** *Counsellor (Employment & Social Affairs)*
Mr Francisco J. Piñanes Leal **m** *Counsellor (Tourism)*
Mrs Rosa M. Gómez Movellán **m** *Counsellor (Agriculture, Food & the Environment)*
Mr Alvaro M. Nadal Belda *Counsellor (Economic & Commercial)*
Mr Rafael Sanchez-Puerta Ortiz **m** *Counsellor*
Mr Nuño Bordallo Sainz **m** *Counsellor (Consular Affairs)*
Mrs Nuria González-Barros Camba *Counsellor (Political Affairs)*
Mr Hector G. Castaneda Callejon **m** *1st Secretary (Political Affairs)*
Mrs Luisa M. García García **m** *1st Secretary (Political Affairs)*
Mr Jamie Lopez-Doriga Gonzalez-Valerio *Counsellor (Consular Affairs)*
Mr José M. García Moreno *Liaison Magistrate (Justice Affairs)*
Mr Jose M. Lucio-Villegas Cámara *Attaché (Home Affairs)*
Mr Juan A. Jiménez Arnedo **m** *Attaché (Home Affairs)*
Mr Andrés Galván Ramírez *Attaché (Maritime Affairs)*
Dr Esteban Pacha Vicente **m** *Attaché (Transport & Infrastructures)*
Mr Carlos Ruiz González *Deputy Counsellor (Tourism)*
Ms Maria J. Conde Solé *Attaché (Press & Communications)*
Mr Jose R. Del Valle Portillo **m** *Deputy Counsellor (Commercial)*
Mr Jose M. Mingorance Arnaiz **m** *Attaché*
Mrs Carmen Sanz Castrillo **m** *Attaché (Commercial)*
Ms Beatriz Aparicio Campillo *Chancellor*

SRI LANKA

High Commission of the Democratic Socialist Republic of Sri Lanka
13 Hyde Park Gardens W2 2LU
020 7262 1841
Fax 020 7262 7970
mail@slhc-london.co.uk
www.srilankahighcommission.co.uk
Monday-Friday 09.30 -17.30

HER EXCELLENCY MISS MANISHA GUNASEKERA *High Commissioner (Since 22 October 2018)*
Mr Samantha Priyadarshana Weerasinghe Pathirana **m** *Deputy High Commissioner*
Mrs Lakmini Priyanga Peiris Mendis * *Minister (Trade)*
Brigadier Dappula Bandara Swarna Narayana Bothota **m** *Minister Counsellor (Defence)*
Mr Christy Ruban Augustin **m** *Counsellor*
Mr Abdul Haleem Noohu Lebbai **m** *Counsellor*
Mr. Senuja Samaraweera **m** *2nd Secretary (Commerce)*
Mr Mohamed Sanoosi Hanifa * *3rd Secretary (Protocol & Logistics)*
Miss Athuraliyage Thivanka Upachala *3rd Secretary*
Miss Thimithu Sanjika Dissanayake *3rd Secretary*

SUDAN

Embassy of the Republic of the Sudan
3 Cleveland Row St James's SW1A 1DD
020 7839 8080
info@sudan-embassy.co.uk
www.sudan-embassy.co.uk

HIS EXCELLENCY MR MOHAMED ABDALLA IDRIS MOHAMED **m** *Ambassador Extraordinary & Plenipotentiary (since 8 February 2019)*
Mrs Rugaiya Shuaib Idris Mohamed
Mr Mohamed Hussein Idris Abbaker **m** *Minister Plenipotentiary*
Brigadier Mohamed Abdelrahman Mohamed Babiker * *Military Attaché*
Mr Khalid Mohamed Ali Hassan **m** *Counsellor*
Mr Asim Mustafa Ali Nugud * *1st Secretary*
Mr Gaffar Osman Mubarak Osman **m** *1st Secretary*
Mr Musab Ismail Mahmoud Ismail *2nd Secretary*
Mr Tarig Abderhim Abderhman Mohamed **m** *Counsellor*
Mr Mustafa Abdelaziz Mohamed Al-Batal * *Media Attaché*

SURINAME

Embassy of the Republic of Suriname
91 Rue du Ranelagh, 75016
Paris, FRANCE
(00) 33 01 45 25 93 00
Amb.frankrijk@gov.sr

Contact Details in the United Kingdom:
127 Pier House
31 Cheyne Walk
London SW3 5HN
(00) 44 7768 196 326
ajethu@honoraryconsul.info

HIS EXCELLENCY MR REGGY MARTIALES NELSON **m** *Ambassador Extraordinary & Plenipotentiary (since 5 July 2019)*
Mrs Haidy Madelien Gravenberch

SWAZILAND (Now Known as Eswatini)

SWEDEN

Embassy of Sweden
11 Montagu Place W1H 2AL
Main Switchboard 020 7917 6400
Passports 020 7917 6410
Visas 020 7917 6418
Defence 020 7917 6426
Passports & Visas Fax 020 7917 6475
ambassaden.london@gov.se
www.swedenabroad.com/london
Monday-Friday 09.00-12.00 & 14.00-16.00

Swedish Trade and Investment Council – Business Sweden
4th Floor
5 Upper Montagu Street W1H 2AG
Main Switchboard: 020 7258 5130
Fax: 020 7616 4099
Email: unitedkingdom@business-sweden.se

HIS EXCELLENCY MR TORBJÖRN SOHLSTRÖM **m** *Ambassador Extraordinary & Plenipotentiary (since 2 September 2016)*
Mrs Helena Vazquez Sohlström
Mr Magnus Stuxberg **m** *Minister-Counsellor (Political and European Affairs), Deputy Chief of Mission*
Mrs Annika White **m** *Counsellor (Administrative & Consular Affairs)*
Mrs Åsa Theander **m** *Counsellor (Foreign & Security Policy)*
Ms Marleen Windahl *1st Secretary (Consular Affairs)*
Mrs Anna Brodin **m** *1st Secretary (Political Affairs)*
Ms Margareta Wrang *3rd Secretary*

Mrs Kerstin Killian m *3rd Secretary*
Ms Pia Lundberg *Counsellor (Cultural Affairs)*
Mr Markus Tegnhammar m *Counsellor*
Colonel Per Jenvald m *Defence Attaché*
Lieutenant Colonel Peter Viklund * *Deputy Defence Attaché*
Mr Gustaf Bergström m *Commercial Counsellor & Trade Commissioner*

SWITZERLAND

Embassy of Switzerland
16 -18 Montagu Place W1H 2BQ
020 7616 6000
Fax 020 7724 7001
london@eda.admin.ch
www.eda.admin.ch/london
Monday-Friday 09.00-12.00

Regional Consular Centre London
c/o Embassy of Switzerland in the United Kingdom
16-18 Montagu Place W1H 2BQ
020 7616 6000
Fax 020 7724 7001
rcclondon@eda.admin.ch
www.eda.admin.ch/rcclondon

HIS EXCELLENCY MR ALEXANDRE FASEL m *Ambassador Extraordinary & Plenipotentiary (since 4 September 2017)*
        Mrs Nicole Fasel-Rossier
Mr François Voeffray m *Minister & Deputy Head of Mission*
Colonel (GS) Martin Walter Lerch m *Defence Attaché (Military, Naval and Air Attaché)*
Mr Alexander Renggli m *Counsellor (Head Economic, Finance, Science & Innovation)*
Mrs Stefanie Küng m *Counsellor (Deputy Head Economic, Finance, Science & Innovation)*
Mrs Manuela Ferrari m *Counsellor & Consul General (Head Finance, Personnel & Administration)*
Mr Marco Fischer *1st Secretary (Head Political & Legal Affairs)*
Mr Felix Schwendimann m *1st Secretary (Financial & Fiscal Affairs)*
Mrs Simona Regazzoni Kwenda m *Counsellor & Consul (Head Regional Consular Centre)*
Ms Andrea Hauri *3rd Secretary (Consular Affairs)*
Mr Matthias Schnyder m *Attaché (Visa Affairs)*

SYRIA
(Temporarily closed by the Syrian Government)
Embassy of the Syrian Arab Republic
8 Belgrave Square SW1X 8PH
020 7245 9012
Fax 020 7235 4621
www.syrianembassy.co.uk
Monday-Friday 09.30-15.30

TAJIKISTAN

Embassy of the Republic of Tajikistan
3 Shortlands, Hammersmith W6 8DA
020 3609 8788
tajemblondon@mfa.tj
www.tajembassy.org.uk

HIS EXCELLENCY MR MASUD KHALIFAZODA m *Ambassador Extraordinary & Plenipotentiary (since 1 November 2018)*
        Mrs Mutriba Dzhabborova
Mr Hotam Qurbonov m *3rd Secretary*
Mr Behruz Emomov m *3rd Secretary & Consul*
Mr Parviz Eshonjonov m *3rd Secretary(Political)*

TANZANIA

High Commission of the United Republic of Tanzania
3 Stratford Place
London
W1C 1AS
Tel: 02075691470
Fax 02074913710
Email: Ublaozi@tzhc.uk
Website: www.tzhc.uk

HER EXCELLENCY DR ASHA-ROSE MIGIRO * *High Commissioner (since 14 June 2016)*
Ms Rose Kitandula **m** *Counsellor (Political)*
Mr Juma Sheha **m** *Counsellor*
Col Jackson Mwaseba **m** *Defence Adviser*
Mr Wema Kibona **m** *Finance Attaché*

THAILAND

Royal Thai Embassy
29-30 Queen's Gate SW7 5JB
020 7225 5500, 020 7589 2944
Fax 020 7823 9695
rtelondon@thaiembassyuk.org.uk
www.thaiembassyuk.org.uk
Monday-Friday 09.00 -12.30 & 14.00-17.00

Consular Section
Basement, 29-30 Queen's Gate SW7 5JB
020 7589 5528
Fax 020 7823 7492
csinfo@thaiembassyuk.org.uk
visa@thaiembassyuk.org.uk
Monday-Friday 09.00 -12.00

Office of the Defence & Naval Attaché
29-30 Queen's Gate SW7 5JB
020 7589 0492
Fax 020 7225 3782

Office of the Military Attaché
29-30 Queen's Gate SW7 5JB
020 7589 3155
Fax 020 7589 3155

Office of the Air Attaché
29-30 Queen's Gate SW7 5JB
020 7589 0369
Fax 020 7589 0369

Office of Commercial Affairs
11 Hertford Street W1Y 7DX
020 7493 5749
Fax 020 7493 7416

Office of Economic and Financial Affairs
29-30 Queen's Gate SW7 5JB
020 7589 7266
Fax 020 7589 2624

Office of Educational Affairs
28 Prince's Gate SW7 1QF

020 7584 4538
Fax 020 7823 9896

HIS EXCELLENCY MR PISANU SUVANAJATA **m** *Ambassador Extraordinary & Plenipotentiary (since 20 March 2017)*
      Mrs Thipayasuda Suvanajata
Mrs Urasa Mongkolnavin * *Minister & Deputy Head of Mission*
Captain Yotspong Dechacoob, RTN. **m** *Defence and Naval Attaché*
Group Captain Wisut Inkham **m** *Air Attaché & Assistance Defence Attaché*
Colonel Seksan Khusuwan **m** *Military Attaché & Assistant Defence Attaché*
Miss Supawadee Yamgamol *Commercial Attaché/Minister (Commercial)*
Mrs Sasiphand Bhanarai **m** *Economics & Financial Attaché/Minister (Economics & Financial)*
Miss Vatcharaporn Ratanayanont * *Education Attaché/Minister (Education)*
Mrs Vipavee Rangsimaporn *Minister-Counsellor & Head of Chancery*
Miss Wichaya Sinthusen *Minister-Counsellor*
Captain Somchai Noypitak, RTN **m** *Assistant Defence & Naval Attaché*
Miss Sirima Maruekaniti **m** *Minister-Counsellor*
Mr Watchara Chiemanukulkit **m** *Maritime Attaché/Minister Counsellor*
Mrs Premruedee Lotharukpong * *Counsellor*
Miss Lasapan Toomsawasdi *Counsellor*
Mr Chatchavarn Watanakhiri **m** *Counsellor*
Miss Piyapathu Ruktanonchai *Counsellor*
Miss Chalermwan Jiriyanapiwart *Assistant Commercial Attaché/Counsellor (Commercial)*
Mrs Pusanee Ruangkajorn **m** *2nd Secretary (Administrative)*
Miss Pantong Poldongnok *2nd Secretary (Administrative)*

TIMOR-LESTE

Embassy of the Democratic Republic of Timor-Leste
6th Floor, 83 Victoria Street, London SW1H 0HW
020 3585 4062 – 020 3585 4063
info@tlembassy.co.uk

(Vacant) *Ambassador Extraordinary & Plenipotentiary*

Ms Felizarda Da Conceicao de Deus *3rd Secretary*
Mr Gilson da Carvalho Ramos da Silva *Counsellor / Chargé d' Affaires a.i*

TOGO

Embassy of the Republic of Togo
Unit 3, 7 & 8 Lysander Mews
Lysander Grove, London
N19 3QP
020 72637522
Monday-Friday 09.00-13.00 & 14.00-17.00

Vacant *Ambassador Extraordinary & Plenipotentiary*
Mr Komlavi Dedji *Minister-Counsellor Chargé d'Affaires a. i.*
Mr Kokou Dokodzo **m** *Counsellor (Financial)*
Mr Kodjo Gbande **m** *Counsellor (Political & Legal Affairs)*
Mr Dzidzoe Megnimabou Mensah **m** *Economic Adviser*
Mr Kpalete Agossou Kpade **m** 1st Secretary
Mr Ankou Gadjekpo **m** *Consular Attaché*

TONGA

Tonga High Commission
36 Molyneux Street W1H 5BQ
020 7724 5828

Fax 020 7723 9074
Monday-Friday 09.00-13.00 & 14.00-17.00

HER EXCELLENCY HON MRS TITILUPE FANETUPOUVAVAU TUIVAKANO **m** *High Commissioner (since 28 May 2018)*
        Major Siaosi Kiu Kaho
Mr Viliami Fonongaloa Lolohea * *1st Secretary*

TRINIDAD & TOBAGO

High Commission of the Republic of Trinidad & Tobago
42 Belgrave Square SW1X 8NT
020 7245 9351 Fax 020 7823 1065
hclondon@foreign.gov.tt
http://foreign.gov.tt/hclondon
Monday-Friday 09.00-17.00

HIS EXCELLENCY MR ORVILLE LONDON **m** *High Commissioner (since 13 May 2017)*
        Mrs Brigid London
Ms Jenny G Thompson *Counsellor*
Mr Glenroy Mathew *Phillip Security Attaché*
Ms Darcyl Legall *2nd Secretary*
Mr Elston Baird **m** *Immigration Attaché*
Mrs Alicia Acres-Youksee **m** *Immigration Attaché*
Ms Esther Millette *Financial Attaché*

TUNISIA

Embassy of Tunisia
29 Prince's Gate SW7 1QG
020 7584 8117
Fax 020 7584 3205
London@tunisianembassy.co.uk
www.at-londres.diplomatie.gov.tn

Military Attaché's Office
Tel/Fax: 020 7581 0952
dmlondres@defense.tn

HIS EXCELLENCY MR NABIL BEN KHEDHER * *Ambassador Extraordinary & Plenipotentiary(since 30 September 2017)*
        Mrs Maha Ben Larbi
Mr Anouar Ben Youssef **m** *Minister Plenipotentiary*
Mr Wassim Hajeri **m** *Counsellor*
Mrs Nour Zarrouk EP Boumiza **m** *Counsellor*
Mr Khiareddine Daboussi **m** *Counsellor*
Senior Col. Abdelkader Adouni * *Military Naval & Air Attaché*
Colonel Mohamed Souidi * *Deputy Military,Naval and Air Attaché*
Mr Cherif Noucer * *Counsellor*
Mr Amara Hosni **m** *Counsellor*
Mr Rafik Ben Henia **m** *third Secretary*
Ms Henda Mediouni **m** *Attaché (Consular Section)*
Mr Mohamed Hichem Sahraoui **m** *Attaché (Consular Section)*
Mrs Karima Boughattas * *Attaché (Counsular Section)*
Mr Errachid Slaimi * *Attaché (Military Section)*
Mr Mondher Yousfi *Attaché (Military Section)*

TURKEY

Embassy of the Republic of Turkey
43 Belgrave Square SW1X 8PA

020 7393 0202
Fax 020 7393 0066
embassy.london@mfa.gov.tr
london.emb.mfa.gov.tr

Ambassador's Office
020 7393 0222
Fax 020 7393 9213

Military Attaché's Office
020 7235 6862
asat.londra@tsk.tr

Legal Counsellor's Office
020 7201 7046

Press Counsellor's Office
020 7235 6968
lobm@btconnect.com

Religious Affairs Counsellor's Office
020 7823 1632
ingilterediyanet@gmail.com

Educational Counsellor's Office
020 7278 6410
londra@meb.gov.tr

Economic Counsellor's Office
020 7245 0434
hmlondon@hazine.gov.tr

Cultural & Information Counsellor's Office
020 7839 7778
info@gototurkey.co.uk

Financial & Customs Counsellor's Office
020 7245 6318
svelidedeoglu@yahoo.co.uk

Commercial Counsellor's Office
020 7838 9167
londra@ticaret.gov.tr

Central Bank of the Republic of Turkey Representative Office
020 7220 9590
cbtlondon@btconnect.com

Consulate General of the Republic of Turkey
Rutland Lodge Rutland Gardens Knightsbridge SW7 1BW
020 7591 6900
Fax 020 7591 6911
consulate.london@mfa.gov.tr
londra.bk.mfa.gov.tr

HIS EXCELLENCY MR ÜMİT YALÇIN m *Ambassador Extraordinary & Plenipotentiary (since 27 September 2018)*
    Mrs Gül Yalçın
Mr Çınar Ergin m *Consul General*
Mr Güneş Yeşildağ m *Counsellor (Political Officer), Deputy Head of Mission*
Col İsmail Candan Aşcı m *Defence & Army Attaché*
Cdr Ercan Hüseyin Eğmez m *Naval Attaché*
Colonel Tamer Tufekci m *Air Attaché*
Mr Ömer Fauk Altıntaş m *Legal Counsellor*
Mr Raşit Yüksel m *Counsellor for Security Cooperation & Internal Affairs*

Mr Gökhan Şahin m *Counsellor for Security Cooperation & Internal Affairs*
Mr Hacı Hasan Murat Özsoy m *Chief Commercial Counsellor*
Mr Tarık Sönmez m *Chief Commercial Counsellor*
Mr Mustafa Süleyman Beşli m *Chief Commercial Counsellor*
Mr Mahmut Özdemir m *Counsellor for Religious Affairs*
Mr Hasan Ünsal m *Education Counsellor*
Mrs Fatma Pinar Erdem Kucukbicakci m Counsellor for Treasury & Financial Affairs
Mr Uğur Kağan Ayık *Counsellor (Political Officer)*
Mrs Arzu Kahraman Yılmaz m *Counsellor for Cultural & Information Affairs*
Mrs Sezin Şahin Yeşildağ m *Counsellor (Political Officer)*
Mr Barış Uçaker m *Counsellor (Political Officer)*
Mrs Ceren Uçaker m *Counsellor (Political Officer)*
Miss Duygu Çelebisoy *Counsellor (Political Officer)*
Miss Ahenk Dereli *Counsellor (Political Officer)*
Mrs Ayşenur Özcan m *Press Counsellor*
Mr Hakan Etkin m *Vice Consul General*
Mrs Gül Etkin m *Counsellor*
Mr Ahmet Enes Tekcan *Deputy Commercial Counsellor*
Mr Mert Sav *Consul*
Miss Özgür Dünya Sarısoy *1st Secretary*
Mr Alper Haner m *2nd Secretary (Political Officer)*
Mr Fahri Kalkan m *Vice Consul*
Ms Semay Kayapınar *2nd Secretary*
Mr Ahmet Rasim Yılmaz *2nd Secretary (Political Officer)*
Mr Burak Aykan m *Maritime Counsellor*
NCO Hasan Yoluç m *Military Administrative Attaché*
Mr Mehmet Muhittin Yıldırım *Liaison officer*
Mr Aykut Andaç m *Attaché*
Mr Kemal Avcu m *Attaché*
Mr Ali Rıza Sağ m *Attaché*
Mr İsmail Yiğit m *Attaché*
Mr Ömer Sarıarslan m *Attaché*
Mr Aslan Karakaya m *Attaché*
Mr Barış Yıldızlı m *Attaché*
Mrs Pelin Tunç m *Attaché*
Mr Arif Adıgüzel m *Attaché*

TURKMENISTAN

Embassy of Turkmenistan
131 Holland Park Avenue W11 4UT
020 7610 5239
Fax 020 7751 1903
Monday-Friday 09.30-18.00
Consular Section Monday-Friday 10.00-12.00 & 14.00-16.00 (Closed Wednesday)
tkm-embassy-uk@btconnect.com
uk.tmembassy.gov.tm

HIS EXCELLENCY MR YAZMURAD N. SERYAEV m *Ambassador Extraordinary & Plenipotentiary (since 02 July 2003)*
        Mrs Djennetgozel Seryaeva
Mr Dovlet Atabayev m *Counsellor*
Mrs Oguljahan Atabayeva m *1st Secretary*
Mr Atageldi Annayev m *1st Secretary/Consu*

TUVALU

London Honorary Consulate (see Honorary Consuls section below)

UGANDA

Uganda High Commission
Uganda House 58-59 Trafalgar Square WC2N 5DX
020 7839 5783
Fax 020 7839 8925
info@ugandahighcommission.co.uk
www.ugandahighcommission.co.uk

HIS EXCELLENCY MR JULIUS PETER MOTO **m** *High Commissioner (Since 30 August 2017)*
      Mrs Eunice Abeja Moto
Mr John Leonard Mugerwa **m** *Deputy High Commissioner*
Mrs Juliet Namiiro Mugerwa **m** *Counsellor (Head of Consular)*
Mr Godfrey Kwoba **m** *Counsellor (Commercial & Economic matters)*
Brigadier Matthew James Murari Gureme *Defence Adviser*
Mr Alfred Tusanyuke Balinda **m** *1st Secretary (Consular Officer & Desk Officer for AU & EAC)*
Mr Sam Muhwezi *2nd Secretary (Trade, Investment & Tourism)*
Mr Moses Mpungu *3rd Secretary (Accounting Officer)*

UKRAINE

Embassy of Ukraine
60 Holland Park W11 3SJ
020 7727 6312
Fax 020 7792 1708
emb_gb@mfa.gov.ua
http://uk.mfa.gov.ua/en

Monday-Friday 09.00-13.00 & 14.00-18.00

Ambassador's Office
60 Holland Park W11 3SJ
020 7727 6312
Fax 020 7792 1708
tetiana.tokarska@mfa.gov.ua

Economic Section
60 Holland Park W11 3SJ
020 7727 6312
Fax 020 7792 1708
economy@ukremb.org.uk

Consular and Visa Section
78 Kensington Park Road W11 2PL
Tel 020 7243 8923 (Monday – Friday: 9.30 am to 1.00 pm)
Fax 020 7727 3567
E-mail: gc_gb@mfa.gov.ua
Hours of Service: Monday, Tuesday, Thursday, Friday 10.00 am - 1.00 pm
Wednesday 1.00 pm - 4:30 pm

Military Section
60 Holland Park W11 3SJ
020 7727 6312
Fax 020 7792 1708
dao@ukremb.org.uk

Press Section
60 Holland Park W11 3SJ
020 7727 6312
Fax 020 7792 1708
inna.yehorova@mfa.gov.ua

HER EXCELLENCY MRS NATALIA GALIBARENKO **m** *Ambassador Extraodinary & Plenipotentiary (since 17 December 2015)*
      Mr Oleksandr Naumenko

Mr Andriy Marchenko m *Minister-Counsellor*
Mr Taras Krykun m *Minister-Counsellor (Economic Affairs)*
Major General Borys Kremenetskyi m *Defence and Air Attaché*
Colonel Vitalii Kraskovskyi m *Naval Attaché*
Lieutenant Colonel Yurii Dolotov m *Military Attaché*
Mr Vitalii Moshkivskyi m *Counsellor (Deputy Permanent Representative of Ukraine to the IMO)*
Mr Oleh Pavlyshyn m *Counsellor (Political Affairs)*
Mr Dmytro Tretiakov m *1st Secretary (Political Affairs)*
Mr Denys Sienik m *1st Secretary (Political Affairs)*
Mr Kyrylo Bohachov m *1st Secretary (Security Affairs)*
Mr Taras Sauliak m *1st Secretary (Trade & Economic Affairs)*
Ms Inna Yehorova m *1st Secretary (Press Attaché, Cultural Affairs)*
Mr Mykola Dzhygun m *1st Secretary (Consular Affairs)*
Mr Dmytro Govoroune m 2nd Secretary *(Social Media, Press, Cultural Affairs))*

UNITED ARAB EMIRATES

Embassy of the United Arab Emirates
1 - 2 Grosvenor Crescent London SW1X 7EE
020 7581 1281
Fax 0207 808381
https://www.mofa.gov.ae/EN/DiplomaticMissions/Embassies/London/Pages/home.aspx

Consular Section
48 Prince's Gate, London SW7 2QA
020 7808 8301
Fax 020 7584 0989

Cultural Attaché Office
48 Prince's Gate, London SW7 2QA
020 7823 7880
Fax 020 7581 1870

Police Attaché Office
48 Prince's Gate, London SW7 2QA
020 7808 8338
Fax 020 7823 7716

Military Attaché Office
6 Queen's Gate Terrace, London SW7 5PF
020 7581 4113
Fax 020 7589 9120

Medical Attaché Office
71 Harley Street, London W1G 8DE
020 7486 6281
Fax 020 7224 3575

His Excellency Mr Mansoor Abdullah Khalfan Juma Abulhoul m *Ambassador Extraordinary & Plenipotentiary*
Miss Rawdha Mohamed Jumaa Mohamed Alotaiba *Deputy Head of Mission*
Mr Hassan Mohammad Murad Mohammad Almazmi m *Counsellor*
Mr Marwan Ahmed Abdelrazaq Abdalla Alnaqbi m *Second Secretary & Head of Economic Affairs*
Mr Ahmed Khalid Mohammed Abdulla Alabdooli *Third Secretary & Head of Political Affairs*
Mrs Hajer Ahmed Yousif Albayraq Alloghani * *Second Secretary (Consulate)*
Mr Abdulla Musabbeh Khalfan Musabbeh Alkaabi * *Cultural Attaché*
Mr Ahmed Musabbeh Alkaabi * *.Police Attaché*
Mr Salem Shehail Salem Saeed Alsaedi..m *Assistant Police Attaché*
Mr Saif Nasser Ali Nasser Alsaedi * *Assistant Police Attaché*
Mr Jamal Abdulaziz Nasser Alowais m *Medical Attaché*
Dr. Suhaila Hussain Mohammed Qayed Ahli m *Director of Health Office*
Mr Abdulrahman Ali Abdulrahman Ali Alharmoodi m *Military Attaché*

Mr Saeed Ali Saeed Saeedouh Alshehhi * *Assistant Military Attaché*
Mr Ali Salem Rashed Humaid Alkaabi * *Assistant Military Attaché*
Mr Salem Ahmed Ahmed Belhoon Alshemeili m *Assistant Military Attaché*
Mr Fayez Mohammed Sulaiman Mohammed Alhebsi * *Assistant Military Attaché*
Mr Mohamed Saif Khalaf Almatry Alkaabi * *Assistant Military Attaché*
Mr Khalid Khalfan Rashed Khalfan Alkindi m *Assistant Military Attaché*
Mr Abdulla Mohammed Ali Almayoof Alnaqbi *Assistant Military Attaché*
Mr Mohamed Saeed Marzooq Khamis Alnaqbi m *Assistant Military Attaché*
Mrs Khafya Ali Saeed Farareh Alketbi m *Assistant Military Attaché*
Mr Rashed Abdulla Mohammed Khuwaidem Alneyadi * *Assistant Military Attaché*
Mr Mohammed Ibrahim A Alshaibani m *Attaché*
Mr Abdulla Saeed Bin Nasser Al Mansoori *Administrative Attaché*
Mr Mohammed Atiq Abdulla Burgaiba Alzarooni *Administrative Attaché*
Mr Sultan Ali Sultan Hilal Alsuboosi m *Attaché*
Shaikh Hamdan Bin Maktoum Bin Rashed Bin Saeed Al-Maktoum *Third Secretary*

UNITED STATES OF AMERICA

American Embassy
33 Nine Elms Lane, London SW11 7US
020 77499 9000
Monday-Friday 08.30-17.30

HIS EXCELLENCY THE HONOURABLE ROBERT WOOD JOHNSON IV m *Ambassador Extraordinary & Plenipotentiary (Since 24 August 2017)*
      Mrs Suzanne Johnson
Ms Yael Lempert m Minister Counsellor & *Deputy Chief of Mission*
Ms Virginia Keener *Minister-Counsellor (Management Affairs)*
Mr Michael Raiole m *Minister-Counsellor (Coordination Affairs)*
Dr Monte Makous m *Minister-Counsellor (Medical Affairs)*
Mr Gregory Burton m *Minister-Counsellor (Economic Affairs)*
Ms Courtney Austrian m *Minister-Counsellor (Public Affairs)*
Mr John Simmons *Minister-Counsellor (Commercial Affairs)*
Ms Karen Ogle m *Minister-Counsellor (Consular Affairs)*
Ms Jennifer Gavito m *Minister-Counsellor (Political Affairs)*
Mr Thomas McDonough m *Counsellor of Embassy (Regional Security Affairs)*
Mr John Nation m *Counsellor (Political Affairs)*
Mr Stanley Phillips m *Counsellor (Agricultural Affairs)*
Ms Seneca Johnson *Counsellor (Economic Affairs)*
Rear Adm David Manero m *Defence Attaché*
Capt Mark Rudesill m *Navy Attaché*
Col Emmett Wingfield m *Air Attaché*
Col Dale Slade m *Army Attaché*
Mr Michael Skaggs m *Marine Attaché*
Ms Wendy Noble m *Attaché*
Mr Brian Bataille m *Attaché*
Mr Demetrios Lambropoulos m *Attaché*
Mr David Kovatch *Attaché*
Mr James Mancuso m *Attaché*
Ms Rebecca Medina *Attaché*
Mr Damian Bricko m *Deputy Legal Attaché*
Mr Samuel Birchett m *Attaché*
Mr Allen Roberts m *Attaché*
Mr Albert Stieglitz m *Attaché*
Mr Adam Boyd m *Attaché*
Ms Jennifer Schroeder-Fawcett m *Attaché*
Mr Donald Voiret m *Legal Attaché*
Mr James Griffin m *Attaché*
Dr Benjamin Harrell m *Attaché*
Mr Dan McWilliams m *Attaché*
Ms Rebecca Tanner m *Attaché*
Mr James Erwin m *Attaché*

Dr Cecilia Leonard *Attaché*
Mr Donald Parrish **m** *1st Secretary*
Mr Stephen Young **m** *1st Secretary*
Mr Morgan Muir **m** *1st Secretary*
Mr Matthew Goshko **m** *1st Secretary*
Mr Mark Jackson **m** *1st Secretary*
Ms Mary Boscia *1st Secretary*
Mr Dwayne Cline **m** *1st Secretary*
Ms Margaret Cadena **m** *1st Secretary*
Ms Ann Gabrielson *1st Secretary*
Mr Zachary Harkenrider **m** *1st Secretary*
Mr Jeffrey Vick **m** *1st Secretary*
Mr Scott Riedmann **m** *1st Secretary*
Mr Timothy Langford **m** *1st Secretary*
Ms Francoise Blais *Attaché*
Mr Thomas Reed **m** *1st Secretary*
Ms Kim DuBois *1st Secretary*
Mr John Bredin **m** *Attaché*
Ms Rachel Coll *1st Secretary*
Ms Mary Calandra **m** *1st Secretary*
Mr Marc Galkin *1st Secretary*
Ms Eman Blair **m** *1st Secretary*
Ms Lynette Behnke **m** *1st Secretary*
Mr Sean Cely **m** *1st Secretary*
Mr Jeffrey Lefler **m** *Attaché*
Ms Dena Brownlow **m** *1st Secretary*
Ms Lindsay Coffey **m** *1st Secretary*
Mr Michael Wofford **m** *Attaché*
Ms Barbara Simpson *Attaché*
Mr John Leuchtman **m** *Attaché*
Mr Mark Lancaster **m** *1st Secretary*
Ms Helaena White **m** *1st Secretary*
Ms Katherine Skarsten **m** *1st Secretary*
Ms Anna Stinchcomb **m** *1st Secretary*
Ms Melissa Zadnik **m** *1st Secretary*
Mr Jason Ullner **m** *1st Secretary*
Mr Jeffrey Patmore **m** *1st Secretary*
Mr James Lindley **m** *1st Secretary*
Ms Maura Watson **m** *1st Secretary*
Ms Anne Lamperez *1st Secretary*
Mr Michael Andruchow *1st Secretary*
Mr Phillip Demske **m** *1st Secretary*
Mr Aaron Martz **m** *1st Secretary*
Ms Anna Martz **m** *1st Secretary*
Ms Beth Kenney **m** *1st Secretary*
Mr Timothy Funke **m** *1st Secretary*
Mr Adam Jansen **m** *1st Secretary*
Mr Jeffrey Hay **m** *1st Secretary*
Ms Joan Grew *Attaché*
Mr Mark Hougaard **m** *1st Secretary*
Ms Joslyn Mack-Wilson **m** *1st Secretary*
Ms Rebecca Haas *1st Secretary*
Mr Jerry Laurienti **m** *1st Secretary*
Mr Gerry Kaufmann **m** *2nd Secretary*
Ms Stacie Constantine **m** *2nd Secretary*
Mr Jacob Grannell *2nd Secretary*
Mr David Conk **m** *2nd Secretary*
Ms Karin Wallace *2nd Secretary*
Mr Stephen Bocanegra **m** *2nd Secretary*
Ms Aroostine Sheston **m** *2nd Secretary*
Mr Yuri Kim **m** *2nd Secretary*
Ms Shailaja Bista Kim **m** *2nd Secretary*
Ms Kristin Mencer *2nd Secretary*
Ms Casey Morris **m** *2nd Secretary*

Mr Timothy Haynes **m** *2nd Secretary*
Ms Elizabeth Sondag *2nd Secretary*
Ms Nimet Soysalan **m** *2nd Secretary*
Ms Sara Moyer **m** *2nd Secretary*
Mr Andrew Veveiros **m** *2nd Secretary*
Mr Matthew Morrow *2nd Secretary*
Mr Daniel Wong **m** *2nd Secretary*
Mr Colin Flynn **m** *2nd Secretary*
Mr John Douglas **m** *2nd Secretary*
Ms Laura Heimann **m** *2nd Secretary*
Ms Bonnie Angelov **m** *Attaché*
Mr David Ubben **m** *Attaché*
Ms Dina Abaa-Ogley **m** *2nd Secretary*
Ms Molly Colbert **m** *2nd Secretary*
Mr Martin Graves **m** *2nd Secretary*
Mr Peter Lau *2nd Secretary*
Ms Laura Davis *2nd Secretary*
Ms Lauren Arestie **m** *2nd Secretary*
Ms Andreea Williams **m** *2nd Secretary*
Ms Julia Landers **m** *2nd Secretary*
Mr Munir Madyun *2nd Secretary*
Mr Gregory Heeren **m** *2nd Secretary*
Ms Karen Welch *2nd Secretary*
Mr Nicholas Dornsife **m** *Attaché*
Mr Stephen Wiegman **m** *2nd Secretary*
Ms Amal Moussaoui Haynes **m** *2nd Secretary*
Mr Judd Meyer **m** *2nd Secretary*
Mr Seann Gale *2nd Secretary*
Mr Marcus Jasonides **m** *2nd Secretary*
Ms Laura Russ **m** *2nd Secretary*
Mr Kelly Graham Jones *2nd Secretary*
Ms Lauren Cerimele-Welch **m** *2nd Secretary*
Ms Ana Himelic *2nd Secretary*
Mr Daniel Joyce **m** *2nd Secretary*
Ms Marjorie Mathelus *2nd Secretary*
Ms Kali Gasteiger **m** *2nd Secretary*
Mr William Hine-Ramsberger **m** *2nd Secretary*
Ms Danielle Winfield **m** *2nd Secretary*
Ms Hailey Hoffman **m** *2nd Secretary*
Ms Sarah Van Horne **m** *2nd Secretary*
Ms Andrea Garbe **m** *2nd Secretary*
Ms Kaitlyn Deutsch *2nd Secretary*
Mr Timothy Moss **m** *2nd Secretary*
Mr Marston Morgan **m** *Attaché*
Mr Michael Westendorp **m** *2nd Secretary*
Mr Jeffrey Kramb **m** *2nd Secretary*
Mr George Tarnow **m** *2nd Secretary*
Ms Anne Savage **m** *2nd Secretary*
Ms Nora Gordon **m** *2nd Secretary*
Mr John Dougherty **m** *2nd Secretary*
Mr Michael Kris *2nd Secretary*
Ms Sarah Tatum **m** *2nd Secretary*
Mr Christopher Tatum **m** *2nd Secretary*
Ms Terri L Mays *Attaché*
Mr Daniel Kight **m** *2nd Secretary*
Ms Jennifer Whalen *2nd Secretary*
Ms Rachael Cullins *2nd Secretary*
Mr Michael Joseph McCamman * *2nd Secretary*
Ms Kristen Maguire **m** *Attaché*
Mr Eric Arthur Wild *2nd Secretary*
Ms Joanna Wulfsberg **m** *2nd Secretary*
Mr Thomas Graham **m** *Assistant Air Attaché*
Mr David MacDonald **m** *Assistant Legal Attaché*
Mr Antonio Castillo **m** *Assistant Attaché*

Mr Jesse Moore m *Assistant Army Attaché*
Mrs Stephanie Elizabeth Roddy m *Assistant Legal Attaché*
Mr Michael Crabb m *Assistant Attaché*
Mr Paul Woodbery m *Assistant Legal Attaché*
Mr Todd Renner m *Assistant Legal Attaché*
Mr Efrene Sakilayan m *Assistant Legal Attaché*
Mr Thomas Kierstead m *Assistant Attaché*
Mr Joseph Cowan m *Assistant Legal Attaché*
Mr Anthony Cook *Assistant Attaché*
Mr Edward Gernat m *Assistant Legal Attaché*
Mr Anthony Mims m *Assistant Attaché*
Ms Kim Marcus *Assistant Legal Attaché*
Ms Laura Curry m *Assistant Attaché*
Mr Anthony Villacorta *Assistant Attaché*
Mr Mathew Katzke m *Assistant Attaché*
Mr Matthew Callahan m *Assistant Attaché*
Mr Alexander Hagedorn m *Assistant Attaché*
Mr Jason Chapman m *Assistant Attaché*
Ms Jennifer Jordan m *Assistant Attaché*
Ms Nicole Willis *Assistant Attaché*
Mr Scott Kohler m *Assistant Attaché*
Mr Scott Stachowski m *Assistant Attaché*
Ms Kendra Wilson *Assistant Attaché*
Ms Caitlin Perks *3rd Secretary*
Ms Nalanthiel Tuck *3rd Secretary*

URUGUAY

Embassy of Uruguay
150 Brompton Road SW3 1HX
020 7584 4200
Fax 020 7584 2947
urureinounido@mrree.gub.uy
cdlondres@mrree.gub.uy

HIS EXCELLENCY MR FERNANDO LÓPEZ-FABREGAT m *Ambassador Extraordinary & Plenipotentiary (since 20 October 2014)*
          Mrs María Carolina Silveira
Mrs Silvana Graciela Lesca Barolin *Minister Counsellor*
Captain Gustavo Pablo Luciani Morlan m *Defence Attaché*
Mr Daniel Mauricio Maresca Boragno *2nd Secretary – Head of Consular Section*

UZBEKISTAN

Embassy of the Republic of Uzbekistan
41 Holland Park W11 3RP
020 7229 7679
Fax 020 7229 7029
info@uzembassy.uk
www.uzbekembassy.org

Ambassador's Office
020 7229 7679 (ext.2)

Political Affairs
020 7229 7679 (ext.3)

Trade & Investment
020 7229 7679 (ext.4)

Culture & Education
020 7229 7679 (ext.6)

Consular Section
020 7229 7679 (ext.1)
08714681100
Monday, Wednesday & Thursday 09.30-13.00
Friday 09.30-13.00, 15.00-18.00

Administrative Section
020 7229 7679 (ext.8)

Financial Section
020 7229 7679 (ext.7)

HIS EXCELLENCY MR SAID RUSTAMOV *Ambassador Extraordinary & Plenipotentiary (since 8 October 2019)*
        Mrs Diana Rustamova
Mr Aliyor Tilavov **m** *Counsellor (Political Affairs)*
Mr Ravshanbek Duschanov **m** *1st Secretary (Head of Trade & Investment)*
Mr Sultanbek Imamov **m** *1st Secretary (Consular Section)*
Mr Shokhruz Samadov **m** *Attaché*

VANUATU

Embassy of Vanuatu
Avenue de Tervueren 380 Chemin de Ronde 1150 Brussels BELGIUM
Tel/Fax: 0032 2 771 74 94
info@vanuatuembassy.be

HIS EXCELLENCY MR ROY MICKEY JOY **m** *High Commissioner (since 11 April 2011)*

VENEZUELA

Embassy of the Bolivarian Republic of Venezuela
1 Cromwell Road SW7 2HW
020 7584 4206 or 020 7581 2776
Fax 020 7589 8887
ambassador@venezlon.co.uk
reinounido.embajada.gob.ve

Consular Section
56 Grafton Way W1T 5DL
020 7387 6727
Fax 020 7387 2979

Defence Attaché's Office
54 Grafton Way W1T 5DL
020 7387 0695
Fax 020 7916 1155

Cultural Section
52 & 58 Grafton Way W1T 5DJ
020 7388 5788
Fax 020 7383 4857

HER EXCELLENCY MRS ROCÍO MANEIRO *Ambassador Extraordinary & Plenipotentiary (since 20 November 2014)*
Mrs Yaiza Piñate **m** *Counsellor (Consular Affairs)*
Ms Silvia Aular Soto **m** *Counsellor (Economic and Energy Affairs)*
Ms Helena Menéndez *Counsellor (Press)*
Ms María Cecilia Toro *Counsellor Counsellor (Protocol Affairs)*
Mr Heli Pulgar *Counsellor (Consular Affairs)*
Vice Admiral Elsa Iliana Guierrez Graffe *IMO*

Mr Marcos García m *1st Secretary*
Ms Petra Ibarra *1st Secretary*
Ms Celina Hernández *2nd Secretary*

VIET NAM

Embassy of the Socialist Republic of Viet Nam
12-14 Victoria Road W8 5RD
020 7937 1912
Fax 020 7937 6108
officeldn@vietnamembassy.org.uk
www.vietnamembassy.org.uk

Commercial Section
108 Campden Hill Road W8 7AR
020 3524 1732
thuyngh@moit.gov.vn / thuynhwork@gmail.com

HIS EXCELLENCY MR AN NGOC TRAN * *Ambassador (since 28 November 2017)*
         Mrs Thi Phuong Dung Doan
Mr Van Hanh Hoang m *Counsellor*
Mrs Lan-Anh Thi Nguyen * *Minister Counsellor*
Mr Coung Nguyen Canh m *Trade Counsellor*
Mrs Huong Ly Tran * *1st Secretary (Education)*
Mr Hung Quoc Pham * *1st Secretary (Political)*
Mrs Ha Dieu Nguyen * *1st Secretary (Consular)*
Ms Ngoc Khanh Nguyen Bui m 1st *Secretary (Attaché)*
Mr Quoc Hai Nguyen * 2nd *Secretary*
Mr Thanh Van Vo m *Defence Attaché*
Mr Dinh Chien Nguyen m *Deputy Defence Attaché*
Mrs Van Thanh Hoang m *3rd Secretary(Political)*
Mrs Thuy Hong Thi Nguyen m Counsellor *(Commercial)*
Mr Huy Pham m *Attaché (Commercial)*

YEMEN

Embassy of the Republic of Yemen
57 Cromwell Road SW7 2ED
020 7584 6607
Fax 020 7589 3350
admin@yemenembassy.co.uk
Monday-Friday 09.30-16.00

HIS EXCELLENCY DR YASSIN SAEED NOMAN Ahmed m *Ambassador (since 26 June 2015)*
         Mrs Nadhirah Ali Ali Sowileh
Mr Abdullah Mohamed Abdullah Al-Jaboby m *Minister Plenipotentiary, Deputy Head of Mission*
Mr Abdulkader Ahmed Saeed Alsubeihi m *Minister Plenipotentiary*
Mr Husam Abdulhabib Saif Al-Sharjabi m *Adviser*
Mr Ali Abdullah Abbas Zabara m *Counsellor*
Mr Ahmed Mohammed Ahmed Al-Bably m *Counsellor*
Mrs Fatmah Mahmood Mohammed Afarah m *Counsellor*
Mrs Raydan Sultan NajiNaji * *Counsellor*

ZAMBIA

High Commission for the Republic of Zambia
Zambia House
2 Palace Gate W8 5NG
020 7581 2142
info@zambiahc.org.uk
www.zambiahc.org.uk

Monday-Friday 09.30-13.00 & 14.00-17.00

Immigration Office
020 7589 6655

HIS EXCELLENCY LT GEN PAUL MIHOVA *m High Commissioner (since 10 December 2019)*
    Mrs Christine Chiyesu Mihova
Ms Millica Nkhoma-Mutale *1st Secretary (Political & Administration)*
Ms Patricia Sikaala *m Deputy High Commissioner*
Brigadier General Oscar Chapula *m Defence Attaché*
Mr Mwendabai Mataa *m Counsellor-Political*
Mr Mukela Mutukwa *m Counsellor (Economic)*
Mrs Fanny Kalebwe *m 1st Secretary (Finance)*
Mr Portpher Sakala *m 1st Secretary (Consular)*
Mrs Ireen Mwimba Chengo *m 1st Secretary (Trade)*
Ms Alice Mubanga Mulenga Shanshima *1st Secretary (Immigration)*
Mr Donald Chamoto Pelekamoyo *m 1st Secretary (Tourism)*
Mr Liboma Lipalile *m 1st Secretary (Protocol)*
Mrs Abigail Chaponda *m 1st Secretary (Press)*
Ms Chitamalika Beatrice Mukuka *2nd Secretary*

ZIMBABWE

Embassy of the Republic of Zimbabwe
Zimbabwe House 429 Strand WC2R 0JR
020 7836 7755
Fax: 020 7379 1167
Embassy of the Republic of Zimbabwe
Zimbabwe House 429 Strand WC2R 0JR
020 7836 7755
Fax: 020 7379 1167
zimlondon@zimfa.gov.zw
zimembassy@zimlondon.gov.zw
http://www.zimlondon.gov.zw
http://www.zimlondon.gov.zw
Monday-Friday 09.00-13.00 & 14.00–17.00

Consular Section:
Monday-Friday 09.00–12.30

HIS EXCELLENCY COLONEL CHRISTIAN KATSANDE *Ambassador Extraordinary & Plenipotentiary (since 25 June 2018)*
    Mrs Sophia Katsande
Mr Elisha Karodza *m Deputy Head of Mission/Minister Counsellor*
Mr Terrence Madzorere *m Counsellor*
Colonel Sternford Kufa *m Defence Attaché*
Mr Zivanayi Katsande *m Counsellor*
Mr Andrew Taka *Consular Attaché*
Miss Hilda Madanhi *Counsellor*
Mr Oliver Mukwena *m Counsellor*
Mrs Esther Kaisi *m 3rd Secretary*
Mrs Miriam M. Panganayi *m 3rd Secretary*

LIST OF THE REPRESENTATIVES
IN LONDON OF FOREIGN STATES &
COMMONWEALTH COUNTRIES

AMBASSADORS AND HIGH COMMISSIONERS

DATE	COUNTRY	HEAD OF MISSION	ROLE	RESIDENCE
29/04/1993	Kuwait	Mr Khaled Al Duwaisan GCVO	Dean & Ambassador	London
24/04/2001	St Vincent and the Grenadines (REALM)	Mr Cenio Lewis	Senior High Commissioner	London
02/07/2003	Turkmenistan	Mr Yazmurad N Seryaev	Ambassador	London
22/01/2008	Honduras	Mr Ivan Romero-Martinez	Ambassador	London
16/11/2009	Oman	Mr Abdul Aziz Al Hinai	Ambassador	London
06/01/2010	Guatemala	Mr Acisclo Valladares Molina	Ambassador	London
12/01/2010	Monaco	Mrs Evelyne Genta	Ambassador	London
01/03/2010	China	Mr Liu Xiaoming	Ambassador	London
12/01/2011	St Christopher & Nevis (REALM)	Mr Kevin Isaac	High Commissioner	London
24/08/2011	Papua New Guinea (REALM)	Ms Winnie Anna Kiap	High Commissioner	London
15/07/2012	Belize (REALM)	Ms Perla Perdomo	High Commissioner	London
14/08/2012	Samoa (NR)	Fatumanava Dr Pa'olelei H Luteru	High Commissioner	Brussels
18/02/2013	Belarus	Mr Sergei F Aleinik	Ambassador	London
28/10/2013	Burma	U Kyaw Zwar Minn	Ambassador	London
23/07/2014	Azerbaijan	Mr Tahir Tofig oglu Taghizadeh	Ambassador	London
14/08/2014	Slovenia	Mr Tadej Rupel	Ambassador	London
01/09/2014	Singapore	Ms Foo Chi Hsia	High Commissioner	London
23/09/2014	Eritrea	Mr Estifanos Habtemariam Ghebreyesus	Ambassador	London
23/10/2014	Qatar	Mr Yousef Ali Al-Khater	Ambassador	London
20/11/2014	Venezuela	Ms Rocio Maneiro	Ambassador	London
15/01/2015	Nicaragua	Ms Guisell Morales-Echaverry	Ambassador	London
22/01/2015	Djibouti (NR)	Mr Ayeid Mousseid Yahya	Ambassador	Paris
18/06/2015	Malawi	Mr Kena Mphonda	High Commissioner	London
26/06/2015	Yemen	Dr Yassin Saeed Noman Ahmed	Ambassador	London
09/08/2015	Mauritius	Mr Girish Nunkoo	High Commissioner	London
11/08/2015	Slovak Republic	Dr L'ubomír Rehák	Ambassador	London
01/09/2015	Bahrain	Shaikh Fawaz Bin Mohamed Al Khalifa	Ambassador	London
11/09/2015	The Netherlands	Mr Simon Smits	Ambassador	London
29/09/2015	Gabon	Mrs Aichatou Sanni Aoudou	Ambassador	London
04/11/2015	Cote d'Ivoire	Mr Georges Aboua	Ambassador	London
06/11/2015	Mozambique	Mr Filipe Chidumo	High Commissioner	London
18/12/2015	Ukraine	Mrs Natalia Galibarenko	Ambassador	London
05/01/2016	Czech Republic	Mr Libor Sečka	Ambassador	London
09/01/2016	Rwanda	Ms Yamina Karitanyi	High Commissioner	London
10/01/2016	Antigua and Barbuda (REALM)	Ms Karen-Mae Hill	High Commissioner	London
30/01/2016	Fiji	Mr Jitoko Tikolevu	High Commissioner	London
02/02/2016	Montenegro	Mr Borislav Banović	Ambassador	London
13/02/2016	Indonesia	Dr Rizal Sukma	Ambassador	London
11/03/2016	Argentina	Mr Carlos Sersale Di Cerisano	Ambassador	London
04/04/2016	Israel	Mr Mark Regev	Ambassador	London
05/04/2016	Georgia	Mrs Tamar Beruchashvili	Ambassador	London
13/04/2016	Guyana	Mr (Frederick) Hamley Case	High Commissioner	London
13/06/2016	Tanzania	Dr Asha-Rose Migiro	High Commissioner	London
22/06/2016	Romania	Mr Dan Mihalache	Ambassador	London
24/06/2016	Hungary	Mr Kristóf Szalay-Bobrovniczky	Ambassador	London
16/08/2016	Greece	Mr Dimitris Caramitzos-Tziras	Ambassador	London
24/08/2016	Latvia	Ms Baiba Braže	Ambassador	London
26/08/2016	Albania	Mr Qirjako Qirko	Ambassador	London
30/08/2016	Poland	Professor Arkady Rzegocki	Ambassador	London
02/09/2016	Sweden	Mr Torbjörn Sohlström	Ambassador	London
02/09/2016	Portugal	Mr Manuel Lobo Antunes	Ambassador	London
05/09/2016	Iran	Mr Hamid Baeidinejad	Ambassador	London
07/09/2016	Canada (REALM)	Mrs Janice Charette	High Commissioner	London
30/09/2016	Nepal	Dr Durga Bahadur Subedi	Ambassador	London
11/11/2016	Korea (DPR)	Mr Choe Il	Ambassador	London

Date	Country	Name	Title	Location
14/11/2016	St Lucia (REALM)	Mr Guy Mayers	High Commissioner	London
21/11/2016	Morocco	Mr Abdesselem Aboudrar	Ambassador	London
22/12/2016	Jamaica (REALM)	Mr Seth Ramocan	High Commissioner	London
25/01/2017	Seychelles	Mr Derick Ally	High Commissioner	London
07/02/2017	Eswatini	Mr Christian Muzie Nkambule	High Commissioner	London
20/02/2017	The Philippines	Mr Antonio Manuel Lagdameo	Ambassador	London
27/02/2017	Kazakhstan	Mr Erlan Abilfayizuly Idrissov	Ambassador	London
27/02/2017	Congo (Democratic Republic of)	Ms Marie Ndjeka Opombo	Ambassador	London
02/03/2017	Spain	Mr Carlos Bastarreche	Ambassador	London
20/03/2017	Thailand	Mr Pisanu Suvanajata	Ambassador	London
27/03/2017	New Zealand (REALM)	The Rt Hon Sir Jeremiah Mateparae GNZM QSO KStJ	High Commissioner	London
29/03/2017	Burundi	Mr Ernest Ndabashinze	Ambassador	London
07/04/2017	Paraguay	Mr Genaro Vicente Pappalardo Ayala	Ambassador	London
27/04/2017	Afghanistan	Mr Said Tayeb Jawad	Ambassador	London
13/05/2017	Trinidad and Tobago	Mr Orville London	High Commissioner	London
24/05/2017	Cambodia	Dr Soeung Rathchavy	Ambassador	London
26/05/2017	The Holy See	Archbishop Edward Joseph Adams	Ambassador	London
13/06/2017	Ghana	Mr Papa Owusu Ankomah	High Commissioner	London
10/07/2017	Belgium	Mr Rudolf Huygelen	Ambassador	London
17/08/2017	Luxembourg	Mr Jean Olinger	Ambassador	London
21/08/2017	Lithuania	Mr Renatas Norkus	Ambassador	London
28/08/2017	Uganda	Mr Julius Peter Moto	High Commissioner	London
29/08/2017	United States of America	Mr Robert Wood Johnson IV	Ambassador	London
30/08/2017	Ireland	Mr Adrian O'Neill	Ambassador	London
01/09/2017	Croatia	Mr Igor Pokaz	Ambassador	London
01/09/2017	Denmark	Mr Lars Thuesen	Ambassador	London
04/09/2017	Estonia	Ms Tiina Intelmann	Ambassador	London
05/09/2017	Switzerland	Mr Alexandre Fasel	Ambassador	London
02/10/2017	Tunisia	Mr Nabil Ben Khedher	Ambassador	London
08/10/2017	Nigeria	Mr George Adesola Oguntade	High Commissioner	London
27/10/2017	Jordan	Mr Omar Bakart Mnawer Al Nahar	Ambassador	London
10/11/2017	Lebanon	Mr Rami Mortada	Ambassador	London
16/11/2017	Iceland	Mr Stefán Haukur Jóhannesson	Ambassador	London
17/11/2017	The Bahamas (REALM)	Mr Ellison Edroy Greenslade	High Commissioner	London
21/11/2017	Guinea	Mr Alexandre Cécé Loua	Ambassador	London
21/11/2017	The Gambia	Mr Francis Blain	High Commissioner	London
29/11/2017	Vietnam	Mr Tran Ngoc An	Ambassador	London
29/01/2018	Italy	Mr Raffaele Trombetta	Ambassador	London
05/02/2018	Niger (NR)	Mr Ado Elhadji Abou	Ambassador	Paris
08/03/2018	South Africa	Ms Nomatemba Gugulethu Pudnixia Olivia Tambo	High Commissioner	London
30/04/2018	Australia (REALM)	The Hon George Henry Brandis QC	High Commissioner	London
28/05/2018	Tonga	The Hon Titilupe Fanetupouvava'u Tu'ivakanō	High Commissioner	London
18/06/2018	Zimbabwe	Col Christian Katsande	Ambassador	London
03/07/2018	Germany	Dr Peter Wittig	Ambassador	London
01/08/2018	Malta	Mr Joseph Cole	High Commissioner	London
01/08/2018	Burkina Faso (NR)	Mrs Jacqueline Zaba Nikiema	Ambassador	Brussels
02/08/2018	Austria	Dr Michael Zimmermann	Ambassador	London
03/08/2018	Chile	Mr David Gallagher	Ambassador	London
20/08/2018	Korea, Republic of	Mrs Enna Park	Ambassador	London
06/09/2018	North Macedonia	Mrs Aleksandra Miovska	Ambassador	London
12/09/2018	Mongolia	Mr Narkhuu Tulga	Ambassador	London
12/09/2018	Chad (NR)	Mr Sem Amine Abba Sidick	Ambassador	Paris
18/09/2018	Solomon Islands (REALM)	Mr Eliam Tangirongo	High Commissioner	London
25/09/2018	San Marino (NR)	Ms Silvia Marchetti	Ambassador	San Marino
27/09/2018	Turkey	Mr Ümit Yalçin	Ambassador	London
28/09/2018	Moldova	Mrs Angela Ponomariov	Ambassador	London
02/10/2018	Peru	Mr Juan Carlos Gamarra Skeels	Ambassador	London
02/10/2018	Cameroon	Mr Fotabong Albert Njoteh	High Commissioner	London
04/10/2018	Tuvalu (REALM NR)	Mr Aunese Makoi Simati	High Commissioner	Brussels
09/10/2018	Brazil	Mr Claudio Frederico de Matos Arruda	Ambassador	London
17/10/2018	Mauritania	Mr Isselkou Ahmed Izid Bih Neye	Ambassador	London
31/10/2018	Costa Rica	Mr Rafael Ortiz Fábrega	Ambassador	London
02/11/2018	Tajikistan	Mr Masud Khalifazoda	Ambassador	London

Date	Country	Name	Title	Location
14/11/2018	Kenya	Mr Manoah Esipisu	High Commissioner	London
16/11/2018	India	Mrs Ruchi Ghanashyam	High Commissioner	London
22/11/2018	Egypt	Mr Tarek Adel	Ambassador	London
26/11/2018	Bangladesh	Ms Saida Muna Tasneem	High Commissioner	London
04/12/2018	Serbia	Mrs Aleksandra Joksimović	Ambassador	London
17/12/2018	Barbados (REALM)	Mr Milton Inniss	High Commissioner	London
18/12/2018	Ecuador	Mr Jaime Marchán Romero	Ambassador	London
19/12/2018	Namibia	Ms Linda Scott	High Commissioner	London
29/12/2018	Botswana	Dr John Gosiamemang Ndebele Seakgosing	High Commissioner	London
04/01/2019	Norway	Mr Wegger Strømmen	Ambassador	London
21/01/2019	Pakistan	Mr Mohammad Nafees Zakaria	High Commissioner	London
31/01/2019	Brunei	Ms Pengiran Rooslina Weti Pengiran Kamaludin	High Commissioner	London
05/02/2019	Dominican Republic	Mr Hugo Guiliani Cury	Ambassador	London
06/02/2019	Liberia	Mrs Gurly T Gibson	Ambassador	London
11/02/2019	Sudan	Mr Mohamed Abdalla Idris Mohamed	Ambassador	London
18/02/2019	Laos	Mr Phongsavanh Sisoulath	Ambassador	London
01/03/2019	Ethiopia	Mr Fesseha Shawel Gebre	Ambassador	London
08/03/2019	Colombia	Mr Antonio José Ardila	Ambassador	London
11/04/2019	Lesotho	Mrs Rethabile Mahlompho Mokaeane	High Commissioner	London
27/04/2019	Malaysia	Mr Datuk Mohamad Sadik Bin Kethergany	High Commissioner	London
07/05/2019	Grenada (REALM NR)	Ms Lakisha Grant	High Commissioner	Grenada
17/05/2019	Bulgaria	Mr Marin Raykov	Ambassador	London
22/05/2019	Maldives	Dr Farahanaz Faizal	High Commissioner	London
03/06/2019	Finland	Mr Marrku Keinänen	Ambassador	London
14/06/2019	United Arab Emirates	Mr Mansoor Abulhoul	Ambassador	London
01/07/2019	Saudi Arabia	HRH Prince Khalid bin Bandar bin Sultan Al Saud	Ambassador	London
05/07/2019	Suriname (NR)	Mr Reggy Martiales Nelson	Ambassador	Paris
06/08/2019	Kyrgyzstan	Mr Edil Baisalov	Ambassador	London
01/09/2019	Cyprus	Mr Andreas S Kakouris	High Commissioner	London
03/09/2019	Bosnia and Herzegovina	Mr Vanja Filipović	Ambassador	London
03/09/2019	France	Mrs Catherine Colonna	Ambassador	London
15/10/2019	Sierra Leone	Dr Morie Komba Manyeh	High Commissioner	London
23/10/2019	Uzbekistan	Mr Said Rustamov	Ambassador	London
31/10/2019	Iraq	Mr Mohammed Jaafar M Bakr Haidar Al-Sadr	Ambassador	London
06/11/2019	Panama	Mrs Irma Natalia Royo Ruiz de Hagerman	Ambassador	London
12/11/2019	Algeria	Mr Abderrahmane Benguerrah	Ambassador	London
22/11/2019	Russia	Mr Andrei Kelin	Ambassador	London
26/11/2019	Japan	Mr Yasumasa Nagamine	Ambassador	London
06/12/2019	Senegal	Mrs Fatimata Dia	Ambassador	London
10/12/2019	Zambia	Lt Gen Paul Mihova	High Commissioner	London
16/01/2020	Angola	General Geraldo Sachipengo Nunda	Ambassador	London
24/01/2020	El Salvador	Ms Gilda Velásquez-Paz	Ambassador	London

OTHER HEADS OF MISSION

-	Palestinian Mission	Mr Husam S Zomlot	Head of Mission	London

CHARGES D'AFFAIRES & ACTING HIGH COMMISSIONERS

12/12/2014	Dominica	Ms Janet Charles	Acting High Commissioner	London
11/03/2016	Haiti (NR)	Mr Bocchit Edmond	Chargé d'Affaires	Washington
08/12/2016	Cabo Verde (NR)	Mr Octávio Gomes	Chargé d'Affaires	Brussels
16/08/2017	Libya	Mr Mohamed A E Elkoni	Chargé d'Affaires	London
30/01/2018	South Sudan	Mr Maker Ayuel Deng	Chargé d'Affaires	London
06/12/2018	Equatorial Guinea	Ms Maria Jesús Diallo Besari	Chargé d'Affaires	London
07/06/2019	Mali (NR)	Mrs Coulibaly Sira Cisse	Chargé d'Affaires	Brussels
05/07/2019	Madagascar	Mrs Anjaniaina Olivia Rakotonirina	Chargé d'Affaires	London
08/07/2019	Armenia	Mr Hrachya Stepanyan	Chargé d'Affaires	London
27/08/2019	Togo	Mr Komlanvi Agbenozan Dedji	Chargé d'Affaires	London
20/09/2019	Timor-Leste	Mr Gilson Ramos da Silva	Chargé d'Affaires	London
07/11/2019	Mexico	Ms Ana Aureny Aguirre O. Sunza	Chargé d'Affaires	London
03/01/2020	Uruguay	Mrs Silvana Barolin	Chargé d'Affaires	London
21/01/2020	Kosovo	Ms Arrita Gjakova	Chargé d'Affaires	London
30/01/2020	Cuba	Mr Julio Pujol Torres	Chargé d'Affaires	London
02/02/2020	Sri Lanka	Mr Samantha Pathirana	Acting High Commissioner	London
04/02/2020	Bolivia	Ms María José Oomen Liebers	Chargé d'Affaires	London
VACANT	Andorra	VACANT	-	-
VACANT	Benin	VACANT	-	-
VACANT	Central African Republic (CAR)	VACANT	-	-
VACANT	Congo (Republic of)	VACANT	-	-
VACANT	Guinea-Bissau	VACANT	-	-
VACANT	Kiribati	VACANT	-	-
VACANT	Nauru	VACANT	-	-
VACANT	São Tomé & Principe	VACANT	-	-
VACANT	Somalia	VACANT	-	-
VACANT	Syria	VACANT	-	-
VACANT	Togo	VACANT	-	-
VACANT	Vanuatu	VACANT	-	-

NATIONAL DAYS

Date		Country	Title
January	1	Cuba	Day of Liberations
	1	Haiti	National Day
	1	Sudan	Independence Day
	4	Burma (Myanmar)	Independence Day
	26	India	Republic Day
	26	Australia	Australia Day
	31	Nauru	Independence Day
February	4	Sri Lanka	Independence Day
	6	New Zealand	Waitangi Day
	7	Grenada	Independence Day
	11	Iran	Islamic Revolution Day
	15	Serbia	National Day
	16	Lithuania	Independence Day
	17	Kosovo	Independence Day
	18	The Gambia	Independence Day
	23	Brunei	National Day
	23	Guyana	Republic Day
	23	Japan	Emperor's Birthday
	24	Estonia	Independence Day
	25	Kuwait	National Day
	27	Dominican Republic	Independence Day
March	1	Bosnia & Herzegovina	Independence Day
	3	Bulgaria	National Day
	6	Ghana	Independence Day
	12	Mauritius	Republic Day
	15	Hungary	National Day
	17	Ireland	St Patrick's Day
	20	Tunisia	Independence Day
	21	Namibia	National Day
	23	Pakistan	National Day
	25	Greece	Independence Day
	26	Bangladesh	Independence Day
April	4	Senegal	National Day
	16	Denmark	Royal Birthday
	17	Syria	National Day
	18	Zimbabwe	National Day
	19	Swaziland	Royal Birthday
	19	Holy See	Inauguration Day
	26	Israel	National Day
	26	Tanzania	Union Day
	27	Netherlands	National Day
	27	Sierra Leone	National Day
	27	South Africa	Freedom Day
	27	Togo	National Day
	30	Netherlands	Official Birthday
May	3	Poland	National Day
	5	Netherlands	Liberation Day
	15	Paraguay	Independence Day
	17	Norway	Constitution Day

	20	Cameroon	National Day
	22	Yemen	National Day
	24	Eritrea	National Day
	25	Jordan	Independence Day
	25	Argentina	National Day
	26	Guyana	Independence Day
	26	Georgia	Independence Day
	28	Azerbaijan	National Day
	28	Ethiopia	National Day
June	1	Samoa	Independence Day
	2	Italy	National Day
	5	Denmark	Constitution Day
	6	Sweden	National Day
	10	Portugal	National Day
	12	Russia	National Day
	12	Philippines	National Day
	17	Iceland	National Day
	23	Luxembourg	National Day
	25	Croatia	National Day
	25	Mozambique	National Day
	25	Slovenia	National Day
	26	Madagascar	Independence Day
	27	Djibouti	National Day
	29	Seychelles	National Day
	30	Democratic Republic of Congo	National Day
July	1	Burundi	National Day
	1	Somalia	National Day
	1	CF	National Day
	1	Rwanda	National Day
	1	British Virgin Islands	Territory Day
	3	Belarus	National Day
	4	Tonga	National Day
	4	United States	Independence Day
	5	Cabo Verde	National Day
	5	Venezuela	Independence Day
	6	Malawi	National Day
	7	Nepal	Royal Birthday
	10	Bahamas	National Day
	11	Mongolia	National Day
	12	São Tome & Principe	National Day
	12	Kiribati	Independence Day
	14	France	National Day
	15	Brunei	Royal Birthday
	17	Lesotho	Royal Birthday
	20	Colombia	Independence Day
	21	Belgium	National Day
	23	Egypt	National Day
	26	Maldives	National Day
	26	Liberia	Independence Day
	28	Peru	National Day
	30	Vanuatu	Independence Day
	30	Morocco	Date of Accession
August	1	Benin	National Day
	1	Switzerland	National Day
	2	North Macedonia	National Day

6	Bolivia	Independence Day
6	Jamaica	Independence Day
7	Côte d'Ivoire	National Day
9	Singapore	National Day
10	Ecuador	Independence Day
11	Chad	Independence Day
15	Republic of Congo	National Day
15	Liechtenstein	National Day
17	Gabon	National Day
17	Indonesia	National Day
19	Afghanistan	National Day
20	Hungary	National Day
24	Ukraine	Independence Day
25	Uruguay	Independence Day
27	Moldova	National Day
31	Trinidad & Tobago	Independence Day
31	Kyrgyzstan	Independence Day
31	Malaysia	National Day

September

1	Slovak Republic	Constitution Day
1	Uzbekistan	Independence Day
1	Libya	National Day
2	Vietnam	National Day
3	San Marino	National Day
6	Swaziland	National Day
7	Brazil	Independence Day
8	Andorra	National Day
8	North Macedonia	Independence Day
9	Democratic People's Republic of Korea	National Day
9	Tajikistan	Independence Day
15	Guatemala	Independence Day
15	Costa Rica	Independence Day
15	El Salvador	Independence Day
15	Honduras	Independence Day
15	Nicaragua	Independence Day
16	Mexico	Independence Day
16	Papua New Guinea	National Day
16	St Christopher & Nevis	National Heroes Day
18	Chile	National Day
19	St Christopher & Nevis	Independence Day
20	Nepal	National Day
21	Malta	National Day
21	Armenia	National Day
21	Belize	National Day
22	Mali	National Day
23	Saudi Arabia	National Day
24	Guinea-Bissau	National Day
30	Botswana	Botswana Day

October

1	Nigeria	National Day
1	China	National Day
1	Cyprus	Independence Day
1	Palau	Independence Day
2	Guinea	National Day
3	Germany	National Day
3	Korea	National Day

4	Lesotho	Independence Day
9	Uganda	Independence Day
10	Fiji	National Day
12	Spain	National Day
12	Equatorial Guinea	National Day
23	Hungary	National Day
24	Zambia	Independence Day
24	United Nations Day	
26	Austria	National Day
27	Saint Vincent & the Grenadines	Independence Day
27	Turkmenistan	Independence Day
28	Czech Republic	National Day
29	Turkey	National Day

November

1	Antigua & Barbuda	National Day
1		National Day
3	Panama	Independence Day
3	Commonwealth of Dominica	Independence Day
4	Tonga	Constitution Day
9	Cambodia	National Day
11	Angola	Independence Day
18	Latvia	National Day
18	Oman	National DAy
19	Monaco	National Day
22	Lebanon	National Day
25	Suriname	National Day
28	Mauritania	Independence Day
28	Albania	National Day
30	Barbados	National Day

December

1	Romania	National Day
1	Central Africa Republic	National Day
2	United Arab Emirates	National Day
2	Laos	National Day
5	Thailand	Royal Birthday
6	Finland	National Day
11	Burkina Faso	National Day
12	Kenya	Independence Day
12	Turkmenistan	Day of Turkmenistan Neutrality
16	Bahrain	National Day
16	Kazakhstan	Independence Day
18	Niger	National Day
18	Qatar	National Day

DIRECTORY OF
INTERNATIONAL ORGANISATIONS
International Organisations & their staff do not enjoy privileges & immunities under the Diplomatic Privileges Act 1964 but under separate legislation, to which reference is made in each entry in this Directory.

m   Married
*   Married but not accompanied by wife or husband

CAB INTERNATIONAL
(International Organisations Acts 1968 & 1981-S.I. 1982/1071)
Wallingford Oxon OX10 8DE
01491 832111
Fax 01491 833508
corporate@cabi.org
www.cabi.org

Dr Trevor Nicholls **m** *Chief Executive Officer*
Mr Robert Sloley **m** *Chief Finance Officer*
Ms Caroline McNamara **m** *Chief Commercial Officer*
Mr Neil MacIntosh **m** *Executive Director, Human Resources*
Dr Ulrich Kuhlmann **m** *Executive Director, Global Operations*
Dr Dennis Rangi **m** *Director General, Development*
Dr Andrew Robinson, **m** *Managing Director Publishing*
Dr Qiaoqiao Zhang **m** Memberships *Director*
Mr André Laperriere **m** *Executive Director, GODAN*

COMMONWEALTH FOUNDATION
(International Organisations Act, 1968-S.I. 1983/143)
East Wing Marlborough House Pall Mall SW1Y 5HY
020 7747 6579
FAX 020 7839 8157
www.commonwealthfoundation.com

Dr Anne Therese Gallagher **m** *Director-General*
Mr Shem Odhiambo Ochola **m** *Deputy Director-General*

COMMONWEALTH SECRETARIAT
(Commonwealth Secretariat Act, 1966)
Marlborough House Pall Mall SW1Y 5HX
020 7747 6500

FAX 020 7930 0827

Commonwealth House 55-58 Pall Mall SW1Y 5JH
020 7839 3411

www.thecommonwealth.org

HER EXCELLENCY BARONESS PATRICIA JANET SCOTLAND **m** *Commonwealth Secretary-General*
    Mr Richard Martin Mawhinney
Mr Senyo Agbohlah **m** *Deputy Head (Secretary-General's Office)*
Mr Nabeel Ahmad Goheer **m** *Assistant Secretary-General (Secretary-General's Office)*
Mr Neil Ford **m** *Director & Spokesperson (Communications Division)*
Ms Katalaina Sapolu **m** *Director (Governance and Peace)*

Ms Pamella McLaren m *Interim Director (Economic Policy)*
Dr Tres-Ann Kremer m *Head (Good Offices for Peace and Political Adviser Caribbean)*
Mr Mark Albon m *Head (Countering Violent Extremism Unit)*
Ms Kimberly Cliff *Head (Finance & Management Information Section)*
Ms Yvonne Apea Mensah m *Adviser & Head (Africa Section)*
Mr Martin Kasirye m *Adviser & Head Electoral Support Section*
Mr Albert Mariner m *Adviser & Head Caribbean/Pacific Section*
Mr Steven Malby m *Adviser & Head Law Development Section*
Dr Brendan Vickers *Adviser & Head International Trade Policy*
Ms Amelia Kinahoi-Siamomua m *Head (Gender Section)*
Mr Paulo Kautoke m *Head (Trade)*
Mr Abhik Sen m *Head (Policy & Research)*
Mr Layne Anthony Robinson m *Head (Social Policy Development)*
Mrs Carina Wangwe m *Head of ITS*

COMMONWEALTH TELECOMMUNICATIONS ORGANISATION
(International Organisations Acts 1968 & 1981-S.I. 1983/144)
64-66 Glenthorne Road W6 OLR
020 8600 3800
Fax: 020 8600 3819
www.cto.int
info@cto.int

Mr Olushola Taylor m *Secretary General*
Mr Lasantha De Alwis m *Director/ICT Development & Corporate Secretary*
Mr Marcel Belingue m *Senior Manager, Membership & Communications*

THE EUROPEAN BANK FOR RECONSTRUCTION & DEVELOPMENT
(International Organisations Act, 1968-S.I. 1991/757)
1 Exchange Square EC2A 2JN
020 7338 6000
Fax 020 7338 6100
www.ebrd.com

Sir Suma Chakrabarti m *President*
Mr Philip Bennett m *1st Vice-President & Head of Client Services Group*
Andras Simor m *Senior Vice-President, Chief Finance Officer & Chief Operating Officer*
Alain Pilloux m *Vice-President, Banking*
Mr András Simor m *Vice-President & Chief Financial Officer*
Betsy Nelson *Vice-President, Risk & Compliance Chief Risk Officer*
Pierre Heilbronn m *Vice-President, Policy & Partnership*

EUROPEAN BANKING AUTHORITY
(European Communities Act, 1972, Protocol on the Privileges & Immunities of the European Communities, 1965)
Floor 46, One Canada Square, Canary Wharf, E14 5AA London
Telephone 020 7382 1776
Fax 020 7382 1771
info@eba.europa.eu

MR ANDREA ENRIA m *(Chairperson)*
MR Adam Farkas *(Executive Director)*
Ms Isabelle Vaillant *Director (Regulation)*
Mr Peter Mihalik m *Director (Operations)*
Mr Piers Haben *Director (Oversight)*

EUROPEAN CENTRE FOR MEDIUM-RANGE WEATHER FORECASTS (ECMWF)
(International Organisations Act, 1968 & 1981-S.I. 1975/158)
Shinfield Park Reading Berkshire RG2 9AX
0118 949 9000
Fax 0118 986 9450
www.ecmwf.int

Dr Florence Rabier **m** *Director-General*
Dr Andrew Brown * *Director of Research Department & Deputy Director-General*
Mr Nyall Farrell **m** *Director of Administration Department*
Mr Juan Garces de Marcilla **m** *Director of Copernicus Services*
Dr Florian Pappenberger **m** *Director of Forecast Department*
Dr Martin Palkovic * *Director of Computing Department*
Mrs Hilda Carr *Head of Communications*

EUROPEAN COMMISSION
(European Communities Act, 1972-Protocol on the Privileges & Immunities of the European Communities, 1965)
Representation in the UK: Europe House 32 Smith Square SW1P 3EU
020 7973 1992
www.ec.europa.eu/uk

Ms Christine Dalby **m** *Acting Head of Representation & Head of Political Section*
Mr Mark English **m** *Head of Media*
Mr Daniel Ambrus **m** *Head of Communication/Partnership & Networks*
Mr Kyle Galler **m** *Principal Economic Policy Analyst*
Ms Caroline Morgan *Political Officer*
Mr Nikolaos Pipiliagkas **m** *Senior Information & Communications Officer*
Mr Paul Kaye *Multilingualism Officer*
Mr Stephen Turkington **m** *Multilingualism Officer*
Mrs Patricia Collette **m** *Head of Administration*
Mr Richard Mason **m** *Accredited Representative of the European Commission to the International Maritime Organisation*

Regional Offices:

Ms Colette Fitzgerald	Head of Office, Belfast
	Tel 028 9024 0708
Mr David Hughes	Head of Office, Cardiff
	Tel 029 2089 5020
Mr Graham Blythe	Head of Office, Edinburgh
	Tel 0131 225 2058

EUROPEAN GNSS AGENCY
NATS Swanwick Centre
Sopwith Way
Swanwick
Hampshire
SO31 7AY
Tele: +44(0)2380401958
Email: jose.castellomoreno@gsa.europa.eu

Mr Jose Castello-Moreno **m** *GSMC Security Implementation Officer*

EUROPEAN INVESTMENT BANK
(European Communities Act, 1972-Protocol on the Privileges & Immunities of the European Communities, 1965)

9th Floor, 125 Old Broad Street, London EC2N 1AR
0207 367 5950
Fax +352 4379 60118
www.eib.org

Mrs Wiebke Jardet **m** *Head of Office*

EUROPEAN MEDICINES AGENCY
(European Communities Act, 1972-Protocol on the Privileges & Immunities of the European Communities, 1965)
30 Churchill Place
Canary Wharf, London E14 5EU
Tel. 020 3660 6000
Fax 020 3660 5555
mail@emea.europa.eu

Mr GUIDO RASI **m** *Executive Director*
Mr Noël Wathion **m** *Deputy Executive Director*
Mr Fergus Sweeney **m** *Head of Division (Inspections, Human Medicines Pharmacovigilance & Committees)*
Ms Agnes Saint-Raymond *Head of Division (Portfolio Board)*
Ms Zaïde Frias *Head of Division (Human Medicines Evaluation)*
Ms Enrica Alteri **m** *Head of Division (Human Medicines Research & Development Support)*
Mr Alexis Nolte *Head of Division (Information Management)*
Mr Anthony Humphreys **m** *Head of Division (Scientific Committees Regulatory Science Strategy)*

EUROPEAN MOLECULAR BIOLOGY LABORATORY (OUTSTATION)
EUROPEAN BIOINFORMATICS INSTITUTE
(International Organisations Act, 1968 & 1981-S.I. 1994-1890)
Wellcome Genome Campus Hinxton Cambridge CB10 1SD
01223 494444
Fax 01223 494468

Professor Iain Mattaj **m** *Director-General of EMBL (Non-Resident)*
Dr Ewan Birney **m** *Director of Outstation*
Dr Rolf Apweiler **m** *Director of Outstation*
Mr Mark Green **m** *Head of Outstation Administration (until 28.02.2018)*

EUROPEAN PARLIAMENT
(European Communities Act, 1972-Protocol on the Privileges & Immunities of the European Communities, 1965)
32 Smith Square SW1P 3EU
020 7227 4300
Fax 020 7227 4302
www.europarl.org.uk
eplondon@europarl.europa.eu

Ms Susanne Oberhauser **m** *Head of Office*
Mr Dominic Brett *Head of Public Affairs*
Mr Daniel Ractliffe *Head of Outreach*

EUROPEAN PARLIAMENT OFFICE IN SCOTLAND
(European Communities Act, 1972-Protocol on the Privileges & Immunities of the European Communities, 1965)
The Tun 4 Jackson's Entry Holyrood Road Edinburgh EH8 8PJ
0131 557 7866
Fax 0131 557 4977
www.europarl.europa.eu/unitedkingdom/en/edinburgh-office
epedinburgh@europarl.europa.eu

Mr Per Johansson **m** *Head of Office*

EUROPEAN SPACE AGENCY
(International Organisations Act, 1968-S.I.1978/1105)
Fermi Avenue
Harwell Campus Didcot OX11 OFD
01235 4444 200
www.esa.int

Mrs MAGALI FRANÇOISE VAISSIERE-SERRE * *Head of ECSAT & Director of Telecommunications and Integrated Applications*
Mr Nicholas John Appleyard **m** *Deputy Head of ECSAT & Head of Integrated Applications and Downstream Services Department*

HONG KONG ECONOMIC & TRADE OFFICE
(International Organisations Act, 1968-S.I.1997/1334)
18 Bedford Square
London WC1B 3JA
020 7499 9821
Fax 020 7323 2336
general@hketolondon.gov.hk
www.hketolondon.gov.hk

Miss Winky Yuen Ling So *Director-General*
Ms Noel Kai Yin Ng **m** *Deputy Director-General 1*
Mr Kasper Siu Kei Ng **m** *Deputy Director-General 2*
Ms Eileen Pui Ling Tung **m** *Assistant Director-General*
Mr Siu Man Chun *Marine Adviser*
Mr Gary Hung Fai Tang *Deputy Marine Adviser 1*
Mr Derek Wing Tak Mak *Deputy Marine Adviser 2*
Ms Jessica Ting Kam *Deputy Head Investment*

INTERNATIONAL BANK FOR RECONSTRUCTION & DEVELOPMENT
(see under WORLD BANK GROUP)

INTERNATIONAL COFFEE ORGANIZATION
(International Organisations Act, 1968-S.I. 1969/733)
222 Gray's Inn Road, 4th floor, London, WC1X 8HB
020 7612 0600
Fax: 020 7612 0630
info@ico.org
www.ico.org

MR JOSE SETTE **m** *Executive Director*
Mr Gerardo Patacconi *Head of Operations*

INTERNATIONAL DEVELOPMENT ASSOCIATION
(see under WORLD BANK GROUP)

INTERNATIONAL FINANCE CORPORATION
(Overseas Development & Co-operation Act 1980-S.I. 1955/1954 S.I. 1976/221)

020 7592 8400
Fax 020 7592 8430
www.ifc.org

Mr Ignacio De Calonje *Director for Western Europe*

INTERNATIONAL GRAINS COUNCIL
(International Organisations Act, 1968 & 1981-S.I. 1968/1863)
1 Canada Square Canary Wharf E14 5AE
020 7513 1122
Fax 020 7513 0630
igc@igc.int
www.igc.int

MR ARNAUD PETIT * *Executive Director*
Ms A Reynolds *Senior Economist*
Mr D Cooper *Senior Economist*
Mr N Kemp **m** *Senior Economist*

INTERNATIONAL MARITIME ORGANIZATION
(International Organisations Act, 1968-S.I. 2002/1826)
4 Albert Embankment SE1 7SR
020 7735 7611
Fax 020 7587 3210
www.imo.org

Mr KI TACK LIM **m** *Secretary-General*
    Mrs Jung-ae DO
Mr L Barchue, Sr. **m** *Assistant Secretary-General/Director, Department for Member State Audit and Implementation Support (D.M.S.A. & I.S.)*
Mr F J Kenney *Director, Legal Affairs & External Relations Division (L.E.D.)*
Mrs H Deggim *Director, Maritime Safety Division (M.S.D.)*
Mr H Yamada **m** *Director, Marine Environment Division (M.E.D.)*
Ms A Gireud **m** *Acting Director, Conference Division (C.D.)*
Mr A Dominguez Velasco *Acting Director, Administration Division (A.D.)/Chief of Staff, Office of the Secretary-General*
Mr C Trelawny **m** *Acting Director, Technical Co-operation Division (T.C.D.)*
Mr V Job **m** *Senior Deputy Director/Head, Information & Communications Technology Services, A.D.*
Mr S-J Kim **m** *Senior Deputy Director, Internal Oversight and Ethics Office, Office of the Secretary-General*
Mr J Westwood-Booth **m** *Senior Deputy Director, Sub-Division for Marine Technology & Cargoes, M.S.D.*
Mrs T Peverett **m** *Deputy Director, Sub-Division for Maritime Security & Facilitation, M.S.D.*
Mr J Matheickal **m** *Deputy Director, Subdivision for Major Projects, M.E.D.*
Mr I Khoury **m** *Deputy Director/Head, Arabic Translation Section, Subdivision for Meeting Services, interpretation and Translation (Arabic, Chinese, Russian), C.D.*
Ms P Charlebois *Deputy Director, Subdivision for Implementation, M.E.D.*
Mrs D Lost-Sieminska **m** *Deputy Director/Head, Legal Affairs Office, L.E.D.*
Mr J A Van der Graaf **m** *Deputy Director, Subdivision for Operational Safety and Human Element, M.S.D.*
Mr T Huang **m** *Deputy Director, Subdivision for Protective Measures, M.S.D.*
Mr P. Sophocleous *Chief, Central Support Services, A.D.*

THE FOLLOWING MEMBERS OF THE INTERNATIONAL MARITIME ORGANIZATION HAVE DESIGNATED PRINCIPAL PERMANENT REPRESENTATIVES TO THE ORGANIZATION IN THE UNITED KINGDOM:-

Brazilian
170 Upper Richmond Road
Putney SW15 2SH
020 8246 4493/82
Fax 020 8246 4495
fianRepresentation.IMO@mar.org.uk

Admiral Wilson Barbosa Guerra m *Head of the Representation & Permanent Representative*
Commander Vagner Belarmino de Oliveira m *Assistant to the Alternate Permanent Representative*

Democratic People's Republic of Korea
73 Gunnersbury Avenue W5 4LP
020 8992 8221
Fax 020 8992 2053

His Excellency Mr Hyon Hak Bong m *Permanent Representative*
Mr Ryong Sop Kim m *Deputy Permanent Representative*
Mr In Ryong Kim m *Counsellor (Maritime Affairs)*

France
6 Cromwell Place London SW7 2JN
020 7073 1393
Fax : 020 7073 1294

Mrs Genevieve Jean-Van Rossum * *Ambassador, Permanent Representative*
Mr Damien Chevallier m *Deputy Permanent Representative*
Mr Philippe Janvier m *Alternate Permanent Representative*

Republic of Liberia
3rd Floor, 107 Fenchurch Street, EC3M 5JF
020 7702 1243
Fax 020 7702 2639
info@liberianpm.org.uk

Mr Isaac Whiekonblo Jackson m *Permanent Representative*

Russian Federation
37 Harrington Gardens SW7 4JU
020 7370 6768/64
Fax 020 7370 0225
imo@mintrans.ru

Mr Yury Melenas m *Permanent Representative*
Mr Murad Nasrutdinov m *Deputy Permanent Representative*

INTERNATIONAL MOBILE SATELLITE ORGANIZATION
(International Organisations Act, 1968 & 1981-S.I. 1999/1125)
4 Albert Embankment, London, SE1 7SR, United Kingdom
020 3970 1066
www.imso.org
info@imso.org

Captain Moin Uddin Ahmed **m** *Director General*
Dr (Mrs) Farzana Ahmed
Mr Cafer Ozkan Istanbullu **m** *Technical Officer*
Mr Halil Ibrahim Keskin **m** *Technical Officer*

INTERNATIONAL OIL POLLUTION COMPENSATION FUNDS
(International Organisations Acts, 1968 & 1981 - S.I. 1979/912 & S.I. 1996/1295)
4 Albert Embankment, London, SE1 7SR, United Kingdom
020 7592 7100
Fax 020 7592 7111
info@iopcfunds.org
www.iopcfunds.org

Mr Jóse M Maura **m** *Director*
Mr Ranjit S P Pillai **m** Deputy Director/*Head, Finance & Administration Department*
Mr Thomas Liebert **m** Head, *External Relations & Conference Department*
Ms Liliana Monsalve **m** Head, *Claims Department*
Mr Kensuke Kobayashi **m** Legal Counsel

INTERNATIONAL ORGANIZATION FOR MIGRATION
Mission in the United Kingdom of Great Britain & Northern Ireland
(International Organisations Act 1968 - S.I. 2008/3124)
11 Begrave Road London SW1V 1RB
020 7811 6000
Fax: 020 7811 6043
iomuk@iom.int

Mrs Dipti Pardeshi **m** *Chief of Mission*

INTERNATIONAL SUGAR ORGANIZATION
(International Organisations Act, 1968 & 1981-S.I. 1969/734)
1 Canada Square Canary Wharf Docklands E14 5AA
020 7513 1144
Fax: 020 7513 1146
finance-admin@isosugar.org

Mr José Orive **m** *Executive Director*
Mr James Lowe **m** *Head, Finance & Adminstration*
Mr Peter de Klerk **m** *Senior Economist*
Mr Kirill Matrenichev **m** *Economist*
Mr Pedro Arruda *Economist*

INTERNATIONAL TELECOMMUNICATIONS SATELLITE ORGANISATION (ITSO)
(International Organisations Act, 1968 & 1981-S.I. 1979/911)
ITSO - 3400 International Drive NW Washington DC 20008-3096 USA
(00)1 202 243 5096
itsomail@itso.int

Mr José Toscano *Director General & Chief Executive Officer*

INTERNATIONAL WHALING COMMISSION
(International Organisations Act, 1968-S.I. 1975/1210)

The Red House 135 Station Road Impington Cambridge CB24 9NP
01223 233971
Fax 01223 232876
www.iwc.int
secretariat@iwc.int

Dr Rebecca Lent * *Executive Secretary*

NORTH ATLANTIC SALMON CONSERVATION ORGANIZATION
(European Communities Act, 1972-S.1. 1985/1973)
11 Rutland Square Edinburgh EH1 2AS
013 1228 2551
Fax 01310228 4384
hq@nasco.int
www.nasco.int

Dr Emma Hatfield *Secretary*

NORTH EAST ATLANTIC FISHERIES COMMISSION
(International Organisations Act, 1968-S.I. 1999/278)
Accurist House, 44 Baker Street, London, W1U 7AL
020 7631 0016
Fax 020 7149 9950
www.neafc.org
info@neafc.org

Dr Darius Campbell **m** *Secretary*

THE OSPAR COMMISSION
(International Organisations Act, 1968-S.I. 1979/914)
Victoria House
37-63 Southampton Row WC1B 4DA
020 7430 5200
Fax 020 7242 3737
secretariat@ospar.org

Ms Susana Salvador *Executive Secretary*
Dr Jo Foden **m** *Deputy Secretary*
Ms Lena Avellan *Deputy Secretary*
Mr Philip Stamp *Deputy Secretary*
Mrs Laura de la Torre Gutierrez **m** *Deputy Secretary*

OFFICE OF THE UNITED NATIONS HIGH COMMISSIONER FOR REFUGEES (UNHCR)
(International Organisations Act, 1968-S.I. 1974/1261)
Ground Floor, 10 Furnival Street, London EC4A 1AB
020 3761 9500
Fax 020 7242 5097
www.unhcr.org.uk
gbrlo@unhcr.org

Ms Rossella Pagliuchi-Lor **m** *Representative*
Mr Matthew Saltmarsh **m** *Senior External Relations Officer*
Mr Peter Grady **m** *Senior Legal Officer*

PRIVATE SECTOR FUNDRAISING (PSFR)

020 3761 8094
Lydia Piddock **m** *PSFR Officer (EUR & ME)*
Hyeon Gyeong Cho **m** *Private Sector Partnerships Officer*

REGIONAL UNITED NATIONS INFORMATION CENTRE
(International Organisations Act, 1968-S.I. 1974/1261)
Office: Residence Palace Bloc C2. Rue de la Loi 155/1040 Brussels
0032 (0) 2 788 8484
Fax 0032 (0) 2 788 8485
Info@unric.org

Mrs Afsane Bassir-Pour **m** *Director*

UNITED NATIONS ENVIRONMENT PROGRAMME
WORLD CONSERVATION MONITORING CENTRE
(International Organisations Act, 1968 - S.I. 1974/1261)
219 Huntingdon Road Cambridge CB3 0DL
01223 277314
Fax 01223 277136
www.unep-wcmc.org

Mr Neville Ash **m** *Director*
        Ms Elaine Marshall
Mrs Cornelia Prestorius **m** *Deputy Director*

THE UNITED NATIONS WORLD FOOD PROGRAMME
(International Organisations Act, 1968 - S.I. 1974/1261)
10 Furnival Street, London, EC4A 1AB
020 3857 7414
http://www.wfp.org

Ms Elisabeth Faure **m** *Director*
Ms Jane Howard **m** *Head of Communications Advocacy and Marketing*

WORLD BANK GROUP
12th Floor Millbank Tower 21-24 Millbank SW1P 4QP

INTERNATIONAL DEVELOPMENT ASSOCIATION
INTERNATIONAL BANK FOR RECONSTRUCTION & DEVELOPMENT
(Overseas Development & Co-operation Act 1980-S.I. 1946/36 S.I. 1976/221)
(Overseas Development & Co-operation Act 1980-S.I. 1960/1383 S.I. 1976/221)
020 7592 8400
Fax: 020 7592 8420
www.worldbank.org

Mr Jakob Kopperud *Senior International Affairs Officer*

HONORARY CONSULS

*Alphabetical list of Honorary Consular representatives of Foreign States &
Commonwealth Countries not represented by a Diplomatic Mission in London.
The persons listed have certain Privileges & Immunities under the
Consular Relations Act 1968.*

BENIN

Vacant

BHUTAN
2 Windacres Warren Road Guildford GU1 2HG
01483 538 189
mrutland@aol.com

Mr Michael R. Rutland *Honorary Consul for Bhutan*

BURKINA FASO

Vacant *Honorary Consul for the Republic for Burkina Faso*

CABO VERDE (REPBULIC OF)
33 Buckthorne Road
London SE4 2DG
a.diasborges@googlemail.com

Ms Anne-Marie Dias Borges *Honorary Consul for Cabo Verde*

COMOROS (UNION OF)
11 Park Place St James's
London SW1A 1LP
07768 821 888
kchehabi@gmail.com

Mr Khaled Chehabi **m** *Honorary Consul for the Union of Comoros*

CONGO (REPUBLIC OF)
3rd Floor Holborn Gate (HRG) 26 Southampton Buildings WC2A 1PN
020 7922 0695
Fax 020 7401 2566/2545

Mr Louis Muzzu **m** *Honorary Consul for the Republic of Congo*

KIRIBATI
The Great House Llanddewi Rydderch Monmouthshire NP7 9UY
01873 840 375/01873 840 152
Fax 01873 840 375
mravellwalsh@btopenworld.com

Mr Michael Ravell Walsh **m** *Honorary Consul for the Republic of Kiribati*

NAURU
Romshed Courtyard Underriver Nr Sevenoaks Kent TN15 0SD
01732 746 061
Fax 01732 746062
nauru@weald.co.uk

Mr Martin W.L. Weston *Honorary Consul for the Republic of Nauru*

PALAU
Bankfoot Square Bankfoot Street Batley WF17 5LH
01924 470 786
Fax 01924 474 747
www.palauconsulate.org.uk

Mr. Q. Mohammed **m** *Honorary Consul for the Republic of Palau*

SAN MARINO
Flat 51 162 Sloane Street SW1
020 7259 9754
Fax 01268 292 629
Consulate.london.sm@gmail.com

Mr Eduardo Teodorani-Fabbri *Honorary Consul for San Marino*

SAMOA
Church Cottage Pedlinge Nr Hythe Kent CT12 5JL
01303 260 541
Fax 01303 238 058

Mrs Prunella Scarlett LVO *Honorary Consul for Samoa*

SAO TOME & PRINCIPE
11 Briary Court,
Turner Street,
London E16 1AN
Tel: 07977 260564
chris.buckwell@btopenworld.com

MR CHRIS BUCKWELL *Honorary Consul for Sao Tome & Principe*

SURINAME
127 Pier House 31 Cheyne Walk SW3 5HN
020 3084 7143
07768 196 326
Fax: 020 7349 0663

MR AMWEDHKAR JETHU *Honorary Consul*

TUVALU

Tuvalu House 230 Worple Road SW20 8RH
020 8879 0985
Fax 020 8879 0985
Tuvaluconsulate@netscape.net

Sir Iftikhar A. Ayaz KBE *Honorary Consul for Tuvalu*

CAREER CONSULS-GENERAL & CONSULS

Alphabetical list of Career Consular representatives of Foreign States & Commonwealth Countries notified under the Vienna Convention on Consular Relations. The persons listed have certain Privileges or Immunities under the Consular Relations Act, 1968.

AUSTRALIA

Agent General for South Australia
Australia Centre Cnr Melbourne Place & the Strand WC2B 4LG
020 7520 9100

Mr Bill Muirhead AM * *Agent General for South Australia*

Agent General for Queensland
Australia Centre Cnr Melbourne Place & the Strand WC2B 4LG
020 7836 1333 or 020 7420 8761

Mrs Linda Anne Apelt m *Agent General for Queensland*

Agent General for Victoria
Australia Centre Cnr Melbourne Place & the Strand WC2B 4LG
020 7836 2656

Mr Kenneth John Ryan m *Agent General for Victoria*

Agent General for Western Australia
Australia Centre Cnr Melbourne Place & the Strand WC2B 4LG
020 7240 2881

Commodore Michael Deeks m *Agent General for Western Australia*

CANADA

Agent General for the Province of Québec
Québec House 59 Pall Mall London SW1Y 5JH
020 7766 5900

Mr John Coleman m *Agent General for Québec*

REPRESENTATIVES OF BRITISH OVERSEAS TERRITORIES

This list is provided for information only. Some of the persons listed below may have an entitlement to certain Privileges & Immunities.

ANGUILLA

Government of Anguilla London Office
The West India Committee
Suite 53, 3 Whitehall Court, Whitehall, SW1A 2EL
020 7799 5441
blondelcluff@westindiacommittee.org

Mrs Blondel Cluff *UK Representative*

BERMUDA

Government of Bermuda London Office
6 Arlington Street London SW1A 1RE
020 7518 9900
Fax: 020 7518 9901
www.gov.bm
kdurrant@gov.bm

Ms Kimberley Durrant *UK Representative*

BRITISH VIRGIN ISLANDS

Government of the British Virgin Islands London Office
BVI House 15 Upper Grosvenor Street W1K 7PJ
020 7355 9570
Fax 020 7355 9575
BWheatley@bvi.org.uk
www.bvi.gov.vg

Mr Eliezer "Benito" Wheatley *UK Representative*

CAYMAN ISLANDS

Cayman Islands Government Office in the United Kingdom
34 Dover Street W1S 4NG
020 7491 7772
Fax 020 7491 7944
andre.ebanks@gov.ky
www.gov.ky

Mr Andre Ebanks **m** *UK Representative*
Mr Charles G Parchment **m** *Deputy UK Representative*

FALKLAND ISLANDS

Falkland Islands Government Office
Falkland House 14 Broadway SW1H 0BH
020 7222 2542

Fax 020 7222 2375
representative@falklands.gov.fk
www.falklands.gov.fk

Ms Sukey Cameron MBE **m** *UK Representative*

GIBRALTAR

Government of Gibraltar
150 Strand London WC2R 1JA
020 7836 0777
Fax 020 7240 6612
Info.london@gibraltar.gov.gi
www.gibraltar.gov.gi

Mr Dominique Searle MBE **m** *UK Representative*

MONTSERRAT

Government of Montserrat
52 Grosvenor Gardens
London
SW1W 0AU
020 7824 5125
j.panton@montserrat-gov.org

Mrs Janice Panton MBE **m** *UK Representative*

ST HELENA

Government of St Helena
Alliance House 12 Caxton Street SW1H 0QS
020 7031 0314
Fax 020 7031 0315
shgukrep@sthelenagov.com

Mrs Kedell Worboys MBE **m** *UK Representative*

TRISTAN da CUNHA

Government of Tristan da Cunha
29 Hulse Road
SALISBURY
SP1 3LU
ukrep@tdc.uk.com
ukadviser@tdc.uk.com

Mr Chris Carnegy *UK Representative*
Mr Jim Kerr *UK Adviser*

TURKS & CAICOS ISLANDS

Turks and Caicos Islands UK Representative
25 North Row

London
W1K 6DJ

Tel: +44(0)20 3691 6997
t.knight@tcilondon.org.uk

Ms. Tracy Knight *UK Representative*

THE LEAGUE OF ARAB STATES
106 Gloucester Place London W1U 6HU
Tel: 020 7317 0393
Fax: 020 7486 7586
press@arableague.org.uk

Mr Ibrahim Fouad Mohielden *Head of Mission*
Mr Sohail Elhouni *1st Secretary*
Mr Saleh Almari *Attache*

INDEPENDENT INTERNATIONAL COMMISSION ON DECOMMISSIONING
I.I.C.D Block 1 Knockview Building Stormont Estate Belfast BT4 3SL
028 904 88600
Fax 028 904 88601

General John de Chastelain * *Chairman*
Mr Andrew D Sens * *Commissioner*
Brigadier-General Tauno Nieminen * *Commissioner*
Mr Aaro Suonio **m** *Chef de Cabinet*
Ms Ricki Schoen * *Office Manager*
Mrs Taina Suonio **m** *Administrative Assistant*

PALESTINIAN MISSION TO THE UNITED KINGDOM
5 Galena Road Hammersmith W6 0LT
020 8563 0008
Fax 020 8563 0058
www.palestinianmissionuk.com
info@palestinianmissionuk.com
info@palgd.org.uk

Dr Husam Zomlot **m** *Head of Mission*
        Mrs Suzan Zomlot
Miss Meisoon El-Shorafa *Political Affairs Counsellor*
Mrs Rana Abu Ayyash **m** *Consular Department*